BEDFORDSHIRE PLANT ATLAS

BEDFORDSHIRE
PLANT ATLAS

by

John G. Dony

BOROUGH OF LUTON
MUSEUM AND ART GALLERY
1976

TO
THE BEDFORDSHIRE NATURAL HISTORY SOCIETY
WITH HAPPY MEMORIES OF A LONG ASSOCIATION

Printed by
White Crescent Press Ltd, Luton, Bedfordshire

CONTENTS

PREFACE

The *Flora of Bedfordshire* (1953) was well received, remaining in print until 1972. Since 1953 the National Grid has become increasingly used for determining the distribution of natural organisms. Pioneer work in this respect was undertaken in 1950 by the Botanical Society of the British Isles and saw its culmination in the *Atlas of the British Flora* (1962), a turning point in the study of natural history This was based on ten-kilometre grid squares which are now the units for national recording. In the meantime tetrads (2 km. × 2 km.) were being adopted for local recording and used by me in preparing the *Flora of Hertfordshire* (1967). The use of tetrads makes it possible to express more concisely than can be done in words the distribution of a species within a given area. Its main drawbacks are that for the less common species the stations in which a species occurs are not given, the name of the person who first found it in a given station is not indicated and no information is given as to how long the species has been known within the given area. These defects are of less consequence with regard to Bedfordshire than it would be with most other counties as all the relevant details are already given in the Flora the substance of which remains unchanged. The work which appears here is a more precise interpretation of much that appears in the Flora with the inevitable additions and emendations made necessary by the passage of time.

My wife and I began our survey in 1970 and continued until 1975. The task throughout has been a joint operation with the recording being primarily ours for in these six years we have visited each tetrad a number of times. We are, nevertheless, grateful for the assistance of co-workers and most especially Miss G. Elwell who took over responsibility for most of the tetrads in the SP92 ten-kilometre grid square; Dr N. Dawson who did most valuable recording around Ickwell Green where she lives; Mrs P. D. Rixon who made herself responsible for the survey of areas around Souldrop and for helpful recording by Mr A. W. Guppy at Bedford, by Mrs A. Berens at Great Barford and Mr C. R. Boon at Silsoe. Our thanks are due, more than anyone else, to Mr H. B. Souster who not only accounted for tetrads on the outskirts of Luton but accompanied me on very many excursions to some of the least rewarding areas of the county. The visitor to whom we are most grateful is Mr P. M. Benoit who has a unique knowledge of some critical groups. Visits to study alien plants have been made by Mr T. B. Ryves and Mr E. C. Clement, the latter also assisting us with some problems of identification. Mr E. Milne-Redhead has lost no interest in the county which was his war-time domicile and has returned to account for the distribution of the black poplar. Assistance has continued to come from members of the Bedfordshire Natural History Society whose recorder for botany I have been since its formation in 1946. It is good to see this society more flourishing than at any previous time in its useful existence. We report with much pleasure that in the final stages of the preparation of this work we have had assistance from much younger botanists, e.g. Andrew Phillips, Douglas Willison. Mrs J. Stevens was most helpful in the initial stages of transferring the field records to the species maps.

We have again been grateful to the various specialists who assisted with the identification of critical species in the preparation of the Flora in 1953 and it is a pleasure to know that after twenty-three years most of them are still with us. Among those of another generation we thank especially Mr A. C. Jermy for his assistance with the ferns and sedges.

A tetrad is a small area which may be defined only by reference to an Ordnance Survey map for which the maps appearing here are no substitute. The indication given on a species map that a species occurs in a given tetrad may be a clue to its exact location as each tetrad will contain a limited number of habitats. This is in one respect an advantage since most of the county is privately owned and the alternative treatment of naming the precise locations may be unjust to the landowners. We have been grateful to many landowners who have given us permission to visit their property and among these we thank especially the British Railways Board, the Forestry Commission, the Royal Aircraft Establishment (Bedford), the London Brick Company, Bedford Settled Estates, Southill Estates, and the Luton Hoo Estate; but these are few among many. It is our hope that others will also seek permission if they wish to examine private property.

We have had the co-operation of the various local authorities and thank especially the County Planner, Mr G. Cowley, who has allowed us to adapt some of the maps which have appeared in the Consultation Drafts of the County Review – the Drafts themselves we have found extremely useful. We also thank Mr W. Harper for his assistance in the interpretation of climatic factors.

Our survey has been by no means complete. An annotated copy of the Atlas will be housed at Luton Museum and Art Gallery to which it is hoped any additional records will be sent. The Museum also has a unique collection of herbaria compiled by previous Bedfordshire botanists and it is desirable that any records of species new to the county should be supported by voucher specimens in the now large current herbarium.

It is sixty years since I first became interested in the natural history of the county and for forty years of these have been the honorary keeper of botany at the Museum. During this period the county has changed considerably. The total content of the flora has diminished but slightly with losses, in many cases inevitable, being compensated for by additions. There are probably more wild flowers to be seen in the county now than at any previous time but this is no excuse for complacency since the loss is of native species we can ill afford to lose. There is an urgent need, more than ever before, to conserve what remains of the native vegetation with the wealth of natural history interest it contains.

I wish to thank Mr Peter Smith, then Director of Luton Museum and Art Gallery for his encouragement in the early days of our survey and the present Director Mr Frank Hackett together with other members of the staff for assistance in many ways. Finally I express my gratitude to the Area Museums Service for South East England for a publication grant which has enabled this work to be published at a lower price than would otherwise have been possible.

JOHN G. DONY

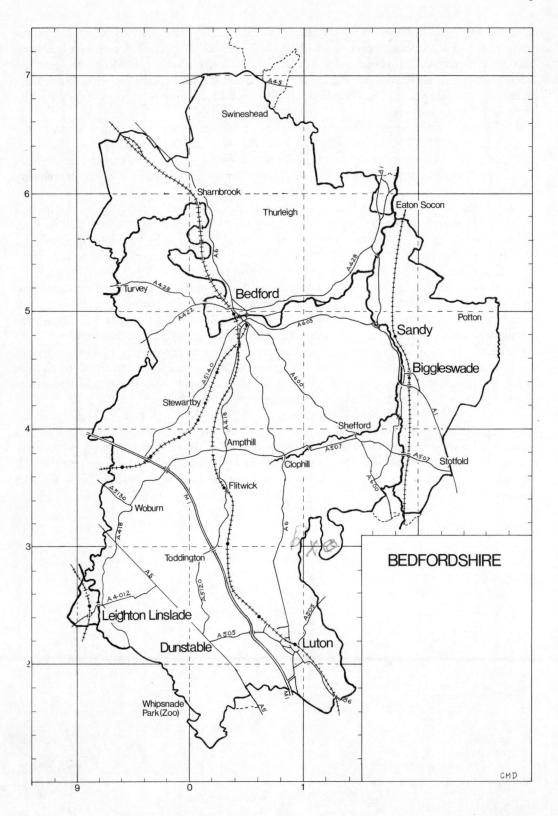

7

6

5

4

3

2

Swineshead

Sharnbrook

Thurleigh

Eaton Socon

Turvey

Bedford

Sandy

Potton

Biggleswade

Stewartby

Shefford

Ampthill

Clophill

Stotfold

Flitwick

Woburn

Toddington

Leighton Linslade

Dunstable

Luton

Whipsnade
Park (Zoo)

BEDFORDSHIRE

9   0   1

CMD

The distribution of Wild Plants in Bedfordshire

Bedfordshire

Bedfordshire is one of the smaller English counties, its distinguishing features being its lowland nature, the great increase in its population in recent years, its varied geological structure, the comparatively large amount of its surface quarried, its few woods, its large amount of chalk downland and the winding course of its main river, the Ouse.

The Administrative County (Map see p. 14)

The boundary of this was unchanged in the re-organisation of local government in 1974 when it was subdivided into four distrcts.

	Area (hectares)	Population (1974)
Bedford District	47,589·0	129,000 (est.)
Mid-Bedfordshire District	50,362·4	94,300 (est.)
South Bedfordshire District	21,200·3	94,800 (est.)
Luton District	4,312·7	164,900 (est.)
Total	123,464·4	483,000 (est.)

Watsonian vice-county 30 Bedford (Map see p. 14)

Watsonian vice-counties are areas adopted by some naturalists to maintain a continuity of their records. This system of recording was introduced by H. C. Watson who adopted as his basis the geographical counties as they were established in 1852. He divided some large counties into two or more vice-counties and linked some small counties with others to make one vice-county. Detached portions of counties, of which there were many, were considered to belong to the vice-counties with which they had the greatest common boundary.

Watson's system is often difficult to interpret. In 1852 the parish of Tilbrook was in Bedfordshire but after the Local Government Act of 1888 it was transferred to Huntingdonshire and in 1974 became part of the enlarged Cambridgeshire. Swineshead was in Huntingdonshire in 1852 but was transferred to Bedfordshire at the same time that Tilbrook became part of Huntingdonshire. The two parishes have a common boundary which would make both part of v.c. 31 Hunts. but Tilbrook has also a common boundary with the parish of Pertenhall which has remained in Bedfordshire throughout. This link makes Tilbrook part of v.c. 30 Bedford; and Swineshead also, as it thus becomes completely encircled by parishes that are all in v.c. 30.

The Watsonian system served a very useful purpose in the nineteenth century but as a result of there being so many changes in county boundaries and the complete disappearance of some counties it has now become so complicated that it is understood by few. In my opinion naturalists would have been wise to have abandoned it long ago.

The precise area of vice-county 30, Bedford is not known but may be taken to be about 121,250 hectares or 300,600 acres.

The Area Surveyed (Map see p. 14)

This is the administrative county with those parts of the Watsonian vice-county 30 now in other administrative counties. It is the same as that dealt with in the *Flora of Bedfordshire* except that since 1953 Woodbury, previously in Cambridgeshire, and Linslade, previously in Buckinghamshire, have been added to Bedfordshire and are included. The area surveyed is about 125,000 hectares.

In the text it may be assumed that records refer to the area that the administrative county and the vice-county have in common. Those which do not are indicated in the following form, v.c. 30 [Herts.] which should read as a station in vice-county 30 Bedford now in the administrative county of Hertfordshire.

The areas concerned are:

A Farndish, v.c. 32 [Beds.].

B A small part of the parish of Wymington transferred to Rushden, v.c. 30 [Northants.].

C Tilbrook, v.c. 30 [Cambs.].

D Eaton Socon, v.c. 30 [Cambs.]. This is part of the previously large parish of Eaton Socon the remaining part of which forms a new parish, Staploe, which is still in Bedfordshire.

E Woodbury, v.c. 29 [Beds.].

F Tetworth (part), v.c. 30. This was previously a detached portion of Huntingdonshire but considered to be part of vice-county 30 in virtue of having a greater boundary with it. It was with E, above, transferred to Bedfordshire in 1965 and added to the parish of Everton.

G Holwell, v.c. 30 [Herts.].

H Kensworth and part of Caddington, v.c. 20 [Beds.] now including a large part of Dunstable.

I Humbershoe and Buckwood, v.c. 30 [Herts.].

J Part of Studham, v.c. 20 [Beds.].

K Linslade, v.c. 24 [Beds.].

L Wavendon Heath, v.c. 24 [Beds.].

M A small part of the parish of Astwood, v.c. 30 [Northants.].

Plant species recorded for the administrative county but not for the vice-county:

Marsh Clubmoss (*Lycopodium inundatum*), v.c. 24 [Beds.].

Lemon-scented Fern (*Thelypteris limbosperma*), v.c. 24 [Beds.].

Heath Rush (*Juncus squarrosus*), v.c. 24 [Beds.].

Slender Bedstraw (*Galium pumilum*), v.c. 20 [Beds.], not permanent.

In addition to these Wood Barley (*Hordelymus europaeus*) was previously known in the vice-county but now occurs only in v.c. 20 [Beds.].

Plant species recorded for the vice-county but not for the administrative county:

Purple-stem Cat's-tail (*Phleum phleoides*), v.c. 30 [Herts.].

The National Grid (Map see p. 14)
The greater part of the county is in the major 100 km. grid square TL and the western part only in the major square SP. The map shows the ten-kilometre grid squares which are now used as the basis for national recording. Three of these have the whole of their area and an additional twenty a part of their area within the area surveyed.

A ten-kilometre grid square has an area of 100 square-kilometres or 10,000 hectares (38·61 square miles or 24·710 acres).

As there is no duplication of ten-kilometre square numbers within the county it is not necessary to prefix the letters (TL and SP) of the major squares in the text which follows.

The Tetrad System (Map see p. 15)
It has become usual in the survey of areas as small as Bedfordshire to divide the ten-kilometre grid squares into 25 smaller squares each 2 km. × 2 km. known as tetrads. Each tetrad has an area of four square kilometres (1·544 square miles) or 400 hectares (988·4 acres).

There are 249 tetrads having the whole, and an additional 132 with part of their area within the area surveyed. Plant records have been made only from those parts of the marginal tetrads within the area surveyed.

Reference is made to individual tetrads by prefixing the number of the ten-kilometre grid square containing it. Thus 03M indicates the M tetrad within the 03 ten-kilometre grid square, it not being necessary to give the full designation TL03M.

Altitude (Map see p. 15)
It is a pity that the altitudes are not related to the metric system as are all other details. The map may be compared with those showing river drainage and solid geology. In a lowland county such as Bedfordshire it would appear that altitude, except so far as it affects rainfall and river drainage, has little effect on plant distribution.

Rainfall (Map see p. 15)
Only Cambridgeshire, including what was previously Huntingdonshire, the western part of Norfolk and the Thames Estuary (coastal Essex and north Kent) have less rainfall than the drier parts of Bedfordshire. Within a limited area rainfall varies directly with altitude and the north of the county is consequently drier than the south. In the lower parts of the Ouse valley (altitude less than 20 m.) the annual rainfall is about 550 mm. per annum but in the higher parts of the Chilterns (altitude over 225 m.) it exceeds 750 mm. The map is based on figures of average rainfall from 1916 to 1950 which are the most recent to be published. These also show that October, November and December are the months of greatest rainfall, accounting for about 30% of the total annual rainfall and February, March and April the months of least rainfall accounting for only about 20% of the total.

There are few statistics showing ranges of temperature, sunshine, humidity, etc. within the county. In January and February the average temperature is between 4°C and 5°C, about the same as it is in places of comparable altitude in the north of Scotland. In July the average temperature is between 16°C and 17°C. The annual range of temperature of about 12°C is higher than any other part of the British Isles except East Anglia.

Solid Geology (Map see p. 16)
The various geological strata and the soils derived from them provide the biggest factor affecting plant distribution in the county. The Chalk and the Great Oolite are both calcareous but each includes subdivisions which if shown on the map would have made it unnecessarily complicated.

The Lower Chalk, the lowest of the Chalk strata, is free from flints and supports a vegetation which is significantly different from that of the Middle and Upper Chalk. The Great Oolite Clay and the Great Oolite Limestone have been combined on the map to constitute the Great Oolite and the Kellaways Rock is similarly combined with the Cornbrash which, like the Great Oolite, is calcareous.

The Lower Greensand is by contrast acid, supporting a vegetation very different from that of the Chalk and Oolite. To the north of the Lower Greensand and separating it from the Oolite Series is the Oxford Clay which provides neutral soils. To the south of the Oxford Clay is a narrow band of Ampthill Clay which is not shown on the map as it is in most respects similar to the Oxford Clay. It is, however, possible that closer examination could reveal minor differences in its vegetation.

To the south of the Lower Greensand and separating it from the Chalk is a narrow band of Gault Clay which like the Oxford Clay provides neutral soils.

The sharply contrasting nature of these geological formations provides conditions which are conducive to a number of plant species having distinctive patterns of distribution within the county.

Surface Geology (Map see p. 17)
The comparative simplicity of the solid geology is to some extent modified by the effect of drift and other deposits.

The Clay-with-Flints, whatever its origin may be, which overlies much of the Chalk in the south of the county is acid giving rise to soils which support a vegetation similar in many respects to that of the Lower Greensand.

Boulder Clay which overlies large areas especially in the north of the county is very variable but much of it calcareous. The only other drift deposit of consequence is Glacial Gravel which in the main gives rise to acid soils.

The River Gravels and Alluvium provide neutral or slightly calcareous soils as most of the rivers responsible for their formation had their origin as chalk streams.

The map is of necessity simplified as some small individual deposits are too insignificant to be shown. In addition one deposit, peat, is not shown at all. It is small in extent and much of it cultivated. A few peat fens still remain including Flitwick Moor (03M) which is still of considerable natural history interest but losing much of its former botanical importance due to a previous lowering of the water table.

Wetlands (Map see p. 18)
The greater part of the county is drained by the Ouse and its tributaries. The Ouse itself follows a winding course of about 50 km. cut mainly through the Oolite to reach Bedford which is only about 15 km. from Turvey where the river entered the county. Below Bedford the Ouse follows a straighter course of about 26 km. to leave the county at Eaton Socon.

The Ivel, fed mainly by chalk streams, carries almost as much water as the Ouse by the time it joins it at Tempsford. The Ouse, recently made navigable to Roxton, was previously so as far as Bedford while the Ivel was navigable to Biggleswade above which the Ivel Navigation followed the course of the Flitt to Shefford.

The only other river of consequence is the Ouzel which for much of its course was the old county boundary. A recent boundary change has brought about 5 km. of the Grand Union Canal, which here closely follows the course of the Ouzel, into the county. The Lea, once a delightful stream, is now badly affected by the growth of Luton through which it now flows underground for about 2 km.

All the river systems have suffered from pollution in one form or another in the face of which the aquatic vegetation appears to have survived surprisingly well.

Open water is otherwise provided by parkland lakes, which are usually fed by streams, and by flooded pits. There are now very few ponds. The flooded pits, a delight to ornithologists, are too recent in their origin to add much of interest to the aquatic vegetation.

There is more open water in the county now than at any period since natural history observations began and there is every prospect that the aquatic vegetation will hold its ground even if its nature changes.

Marshes and similar wet areas have been diminished by a number of causes including drainage, a lowering of the water table, the dredging of water courses, lack of grazing and the growth of towns. The vast majority of the native plants lost to the county during the past two centuries have been those of the marshes and water meadows.

Chalk Downland (Map see p. 18)
This is one of the distinctive features of the county. In addition to its natural history interest it includes by common consent the scenically most attractive areas of the Bedford-shire countryside and it is fortunate that the public has access to the greater part of it.

The downland has deteriorated during the past forty years through lack of grazing by sheep. This has been followed by an extension of the coarse Upright Brome (*Bromus erectus*) and by hawthorn scrub. Some parts have been kept in more or less their former condition by manage-ment or by trampling with the result that there is little loss of chalk downland species although many have diminished in quantity. An exception must be made for a few species normally found in marshes – Common Butterwort (*Pinguicula vulgaris*), Grass-of-Parnassus (*Parnassia palustris*) and Flea Sedge (*Carex pulicaris*) – all long since gone but their passing compensated for in recent discoveries on the downland of Marsh Helleborine (*Epipactis palustris*) and *Gymnadenia conopsea* subsp. *densiflora*.

Woodland (Map see p. 19)
A survey made by the Bedfordshire County Council in 1971 showed that there were 522 woods in the county with an area of more than one hectare and having a total area of 5,022 hectares (4% of the area of the county) which must be compared with the total cover of woodland for the country as a whole of 8%. There was an additional 260 hectares of small woods and spinneys having an area of between 0·5 and 1·0 hectares.

There are two main areas of woodland:
1 associated with the Oolite and extending to the Boulder Clay in the north of the county. This is natural or semi-natural woodland with oak closely associated with ash, an understorey of maple and hazel and a rich ground flora.
2 associated with the Lower Greensand, the light soils of which are suitable for conifers. This contains the greatest area of commercial woodland although some of the broad-leaf woodland, usually on the shallow caps of clay over-lying the Lower Greensand, is among the finest in the county.

The beechwoods of the Chilterns do not extend into Bedfordshire but a few woods associated with the Clay-with-Flints in the south of the county are different from the rest with hornbeam and cherry standards. Otherwise there are poplar plantations mainly in the Ouse valley.

The Forestry Commission controls 834 hectares (17% of the total) pursuing generally a policy of mixed hard and coniferous woodland while local authorities, principally the County Council, own 59 hectares (2% of the total) held mainly for amenity purposes.

The future of the woodlands having a natural history interest is somewhat precarious as the Forestry Aspect Report of the County Council observes that 'about 1,130 hectares of woodland are of no obvious value to their owners'. This is 20% of the total woodland but over 30% of the natural or semi-natural woodland. The loss of wood-land has, however, been slight and due mostly to the clear felling of woods to bring them under the plough. It must be regretted that this was the fate of two of the oldest and best woods in the county in 1973 – Plant a Tree Year!

Railways (Map see p. 19)
These add considerably to the flora especially in the colonist vegetation of the sides of cuttings made through various geological formations and similarly in the vegetation of embankments formed with earth excavated from these cuttings. Ballast, especially in the neighbourhood of disused stations and goods sidings, provides a well-drained habitat conducive to a number of plant species. The brickwork of railway bridges and retaining walls is likewise the most favoured habitat of other species, including a number of our ferns.

Stretches of disused line have been purchased by various new owners many of whom have incorporated them into their adjacent farmland. Parts of the old cuttings, embank-ments, sidings and brickwork which remain have a vegeta-tion similar to that of their counterparts on the lines still in use. This, however, has every evidence of being short-lived.

A few plant species occur in the county only in habitats provided by the railway and others are more abundant in these habitats than elsewhere.

Mineral workings (Map see p. 20)
These have increased considerably in recent years. The Minerals Aspect Report of the County Council (1972) noted over two hundred workings either in use or aban-doned. These include not only the larger pits in use or recently abandoned shown on the map but numerous small sand and gravel pits, lime workings etc. long since aban-doned and in many instances partially restored.

Chalk workings. These are slow to colonise but when they do so the result is a very rich vegetation as may be seen on the spoil heaps at Sundon (02IJP) and Sewell (92W). Flooded pits are comparatively new but a previously flooded pit developed a calcareous marsh flora on its shores before it was filled in.

Clay workings. Those on the Oxford Clay constituting the largest area of quarrying in the county are for brick making and the few on the Gault Clay mainly for tile manufacture. Clay pits are slow to colonise and there is no instance in the county of colonisation having pro-ceeded far. There is, however, evidence that given time they will produce a rich vegetation as some interesting indicator species have already arrived. The flooded pits, of which there are many, have so far produced only an insignificant aquatic vegetation.

Sand and gravel workings. Although these are varied in their nature their colonisation by plant growth is so similar that they are best considered as a whole. They all colonise rapidly with minor variations depending partly on geological factors. The river-gravel pits have on the whole a more calcareous vegetation than the sand and fuller's earth quarries and indeed these latter may develop an almost heath-like vegetation. The compactness of the soil remaining when the workings are finished is a factor in determining the nature of the colonisation since perennials take control quickly of the spoil heaps leaving annuals to survive on the floors of the quarries. The rapid colonisation of these various workings makes their botanical interest greatest in their early stages as there is usually a relatively quick succession to rank grass and bushes. Flooded pits become colonised equally rapidly and in the initial stages of this colonisation are often of considerable interest. They silt up much more quickly than those on the clay usually without the redeeming feature of becoming temporary marshes. Generalisation is, how-ever, difficult as the pits are so very varied and a few in the Ivel valley have evidence of a continued botanical interest.

Limestone workings. Large pits are too few and too recent to make it possible to estimate their botanical interest.

Much as they may be deplored as desecrating the Bedfordshire countryside, mineral workings increase greatly the number of places in which wild plants can grow and in doing so add to the general natural history interest of the county.

Built-up Areas (Maps see p. 21)

The increase in the population of the county may be compared with that of the country as a whole (the percentage increase at each stage is shown in brackets).

England and Wales (000)	Bedfordshire	Luton
1801	8,893	63,393	3,095
1851	17,928 (100%)	124,478 (96%)	12,787 (312%)
1901	32,528 (81%)	171,174 (38%)	38,926 (204%)
1951	43,758 (34%)	311,937 (82%)	110,381 (186%)
1971	48,594 (11%)	463,493 (49%)	161,178 (27%)

Built-up areas are by no means devoid of plant growth as they contain within them open spaces such as public parks, playing fields, recreation grounds and cemeteries in which a native vegetation may survive. Gardens, whether private or public, will provide their unique quota of weeds. Above all there are waste places on the margins of towns awaiting development and within the towns themselves as old buildings are demolished pending the erection of new. These waste places are readily colonised by plants, many of which are comparatively recent introductions into Britain.

The Alien Flora (Map see p. 21)

This is a considerable part of the total flora of the county. Much of it arises from factors the county has in common with all others especially those with a large population. Alien species may be introduced with raw materials used in industrial processes and with the surplus of commodities used by the general public including bird-seed mixtures and foodstuffs. The alien plants may appear almost anywhere but will be a feature of refuse tips which will also provide garden escapes. The larger refuse tips are shown on the map and one calls for some attention. Sundon Dump (02IJ), now disused, was for many years used by two north London boroughs. It produced a number of species not regular members of the flora.

Bedfordshire has an unusual means for the introduction of alien species in the use of wool waste (shoddy) as a fertiliser in the large area devoted to market gardening. As much of the wool comes from Australasia and South Africa alien species are introduced although many had their origin as fodder plants in the Mediterranean lands. The wool alien species are not permanent here so their distribution is a matter of only passing interest. Among the more frequent species are *Ammi majus*, *Erodium moschatum*, *Medicago arabica*, *M. minima*, *Tagetes minuta*, *Trifolium angustifolium* and *Xanthium spinosum* but a number of species have appeared only once.

The interpretation of the wool alien flora presents some difficulties as some native species occur also as wool aliens, usually Mediterranean strains, and the use of wool waste is not of necessity the sole means of their introduction. They appear also on refuse tips when perhaps they should be considered as casuals.

The alien flora is of little importance but must be accounted for as many of the familiar plants of the countryside had their introduction either as aliens or as garden escapes. It is also extremely difficult to decide what one should include and what ignore. It would appear wise to include all leaving the reader to form his own conclusions.

Floristic Richness (Map see p. 21)

The number of species which may be found in a tetrad depends mainly on the number of habitats it contains. Woodland, hedgerows, rivers, marshes, pastures including roadside verges, railways, waste ground, gardens and arable land may all add species and tetrads having the greater number of these may be expected to be more floristically rich than those with fewer.

In common with workers making similar surveys it has been our experience in both Bedfordshire and Hertfordshire that the most unpromising tetrads will with continued investigation provide a minimum of 200 species. We made this our target for every tetrad to the neglect of some floristically rich tetrads which undoubtedly, with the same amount of attention as that given to the less rich tetrads, would have provided more species than were actually found. Notwithstanding this deficiency the map gives a clear indication of those parts of the county which have a rich flora as well as those with a correspondingly poor one.

The relatively large number of species recorded for a few tetrads in the market-gardening areas of the Lower Greensand and the lower Ouse and Ivel valleys includes some wool alien species. To have excluded these without also excluding the casuals and garden escapes of refuse tips and waste places near to towns would have caused complications in deciding which species should be included. The market-gardening areas with their varied crops are in any case much richer in wild species than the large areas of the county devoted to a mono-culture, e.g. wheat.

At the end of the survey we had, with the assistance of our co-workers, made in six years a total of 88,544 records related to the tetrad system. For the 249 tetrads having the whole of their area within the area surveyed the average number of species recorded was 262 and for the 132 marginal tetrads, having only part of their area within that surveyed, the average number of species recorded was 177. Some of the marginal tetrads have an insignificant part of their area in the 'county' from which it was not considered profitable to collect records. The average number of species recorded from those marginal tetrads for which records were made was 218.

The results of the Bedfordshire survey are closely comparable with the survey made over a period of nine years in Hertfordshire, which is a third as big again as Bedfordshire. The corresponding figures here were: total records 117,703; average number of species recorded for 335 tetrads having the whole of their area within that surveyed 261; average number of species recorded for 172 marginal tetrads 176.

Natural Regions (Map see p. 15)

These were adopted in the *Flora of Bedfordshire* for an interpretation of the natural vegetation of the county. A study of the distribution maps of species shows that most of the regions support a distinct vegetation and a comparison with the map showing floristic richness shows that some regions have a richer vegetation than others.

The boundaries of the regions are arbitrary there being nothing visible in the field by which they may be recognised. It was partly for this reason that they were rejected in the Flora as a basis for determining distribution in favour of a division of the county based on river drainage systems. It is hoped that the more detailed distribution patterns revealed by the use of the tetrad is preferable to a determination of distribution based on either natural regions or river drainage.

The natural regions are:

A *Northern Uplands.*

B *Northern Oxford Clay* much of which is overlain with Boulder Clay.

C *Upper Ouse* much influenced by the Oolite.

D *Lower Ouse and Ivel Valley* which is different in its vegetation from the Upper Ouse.

E *Southern Oxford Clay* which is much affected by quarrying for brick making.

F *Lower Greensand* in two portions with slight differences in vegetation.

G *Gault and Chalk Marl.*

H *Chalk.*

I *Clay-with-Flints and Lea Valley* combined to avoid making two small regions.

Access to the Bedfordshire countryside

Compared with Hertfordshire and the south of Buckinghamshire there is a deplorable lack of access to the Bedfordshire countryside, a feature it has in common with Northamptonshire and Cambridgeshire. It is the awareness of this which has led local authorities in recent years to purchase sites to which there is access, or will be. Many landowners also allow access to sites which they are fully entitled to withdraw at any time.

Among the sites with public access the following have a natural history interest:

Chalk downland: Dunstable Downs (Beds. C.C.) with its extension, Bison Hill (National Trust) 92Z, 01E, 02A; Totternhoe Knolls (Beds. C.C.) 92RV; Sharpenhoe Clapper (National Trust) 02U, 03Q; Warden and Galley Hills (Luton Borough) 02XY; Luton Downs (Luton Borough) 02Q. There is no public access to Knocking Hoe, 13F, the county's only National Nature Reserve.

Heaths: Stockgrove (Beds. C.C.) 92E; Ampthill Park and Cooper's Hill (Mid-Beds. District C.) 03IJ; Whipsnade Heath (Beds. C.C.) 01DE.

Woods: Putnoe Wood (Bedford District C.) 05R. The Forestry Commission allows limited access to some of its woods.

Wetlands: There is limited access to the Grand Union Canal by the towpath and to the riverside meadows between Bedford and Cardington Mill. There is little access to the Ouse elsewhere. Flitwick Moor, 03M, and Felmersham gravel pits, 95Z, are nature reserves owned by the Bedfordshire and Huntingdonshire Naturalists' Trust with access by membership.

This apparent lack of access may be remedied to some extent by an intelligent use of the more recent Ordnance Survey maps on which the rights of way by footpath and bridleway are clearly shown. Many cross downland or heath, pass through or by the side of woods and lead one along riversides. It is much to be regretted that these rights of way are not shown for the northern half of the county where the need for them to be shown is the greatest.

Changes in the flora

The summary below gives the periods during which some native or presumed native plants were last recorded in the county. We are in a better position to account for these losses than would be the case in most other counties as Abbot finished his survey towards the end of the eighteenth century since when there has been continuity of recording. Species listed under wetlands include those depending on a relatively high water table and some of these would have been lost in the course of time apart from drainage operations, the main cause of their loss.

Lost between 1801 and 1850: 17 species

Wetlands: Moonwort *(Botrychium lunaria)*, Alternate-leaved Golden-saxifrage *(Chrysosplenium alternifolium)*, Great Sundew *(Drosera anglica)*, Needle Spike-rush *(Eleocharis acicularis)*, Rough Horsetail *(Equisetum hyemale)*, Wood Horsetail *(E. sylvaticum)*, Bog Orchid *(Hammarbya paludosa)*, Marsh St. John's-wort *(Hypericum elodes)*, Bog Asphodel *(Narthecium ossifragum)*, White Beak-sedge *(Rhynchospora alba)*, Black Bog-rush *(Schoenus nigricans)*, Deergrass *(Scirpus cespitosus)*, Lesser Bladderwort *(Utricularia minor)*, Cranberry *(Vaccinium oxycoccos)*.

Grasslands: Maiden Pink *(Dianthus deltoides)*, Early Spider-orchid *(Ophrys sphegodes)*, Downy Woundwort *(Stachys germanica)*.

This was the period when many marshes and all the remaining bogs of the county were drained.

Lost between 1851 and 1900: 8 species

Wetlands: Flea Sedge *(Carex pulicaris)*, Bog Pondweed *(Potamogeton polygonifolius)*, Small Fleabane *(Pulicaria vulgaris)*, Alternate Water-milfoil *(Myriophyllum alterniflorum)*.

Chalk downland: Juniper *(Juniperus communis)*.

Heaths: Petty Whin *(Genista anglica)*.

Woods: Common Wintergreen *(Pyrola minor)*.

This was a period of little change with the influence of man scarcely felt.

Lost between 1901 and 1950: 13 species

Wetlands: Tufted-sedge *(Carex elata)*, Round-leaved Sundew *(Drosera rotundifolia)*, Cross-leaved Heath *(Erica tetralix)*, Pennyroyal *(Mentha pulegium)*, Grass-of-Parnassus *(Parnassia palustris)*, Marsh Lousewort *(Pedicularis palustris)*, Common Butterwort *(Pinguicula vulgaris)*, Knotted Pearlwort *(Sagina nodosa)*.

Chalk downland: Mountain Everlasting *(Antennaria dioica)*.

Heaths: Lamb's Succory *(Arnoseris minima)*, Smooth Cat's-ear *(Hypochoeris glabra)*, Upright Chickweed *(Moenchia erecta)*.

Woods: Columbine *(Aquilegia vulgaris)*.

The impact of man is again being felt. The loss of heath species is mainly due to planting of heaths with conifers.

Lost between 1951 and 1975: 14 species

Wetlands: Bog Pimpernel *(Anagallis tenella)*, Wild Celery *(Apium graveolens)*, Common Yellow-sedge *(Carex demissa)*, Tawny Sedge *(C. hostiana)*, Long-stalked Yellow-sedge *(C. lepidocarpa)*, Caraway *(Carum carvi)*, Heath Spotted-orchid *(Dactylorhiza maculata)*, Fritillary *(Fritillaria meleagris)*, Mudwort *(Limosella aquatica)*, Lousewort *(Pedicularis sylvatica)*.

Heaths: Green-ribbed Sedge *(Carex binervis)*, White Sedge *(C. curta)*, Dodder *(Cuscuta epithymum)*, Mat-grass *(Nardus stricta)*.

These are species known in the county in 1953 but which we have been unable to find during the past six years. It is to be hoped that some may still be here but have eluded us. Others have definitely been lost, we fear unnecessarily. Plant species are now being lost at a greater rate than ever before with a number of interesting ones hanging on in a precarious situation.

It is good to note that woodland species have stood up well to the changing conditions and the chalk downland species better still. There are indeed more species on the downland now than were known to the earlier botanists.

Some interesting species still remain in the county, six probably in greater abundance than in any other:

Great Pignut *(Bunium bulbocastanum)*, which should continue to thrive so long as there is waste ground on the Chalk around Luton and Dunstable, its headquarters in Britain.

Spiked Star-of-Bethlehem *(Ornithogalum pyrenaicum)*, which is still as abundant to the west of Eaton Socon as it was when eighteenth century botanists first recorded it there.

Grey Mouse-ear *(Cerastium brachypetalum)*, still to be found at Wymington where it was first recorded for the British Isles in 1946 and must now be presumed to be a native species.

Moon Carrot *(Seseli libanotis)* and Spotted Cat's-ear *(Hypochoeris maculata)*, both happily conserved in Knocking Hoe National Nature Reserve.

Field Cow-wheat *(Melampyrum arvense)*, still surviving in its Bedfordshire stations but being a semi-parasitic annual very difficult to conserve.

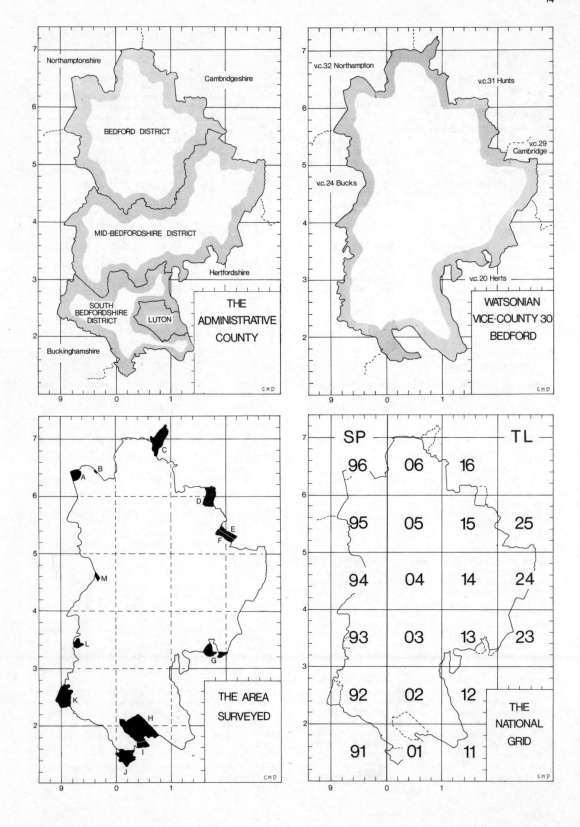

THE ADMINISTRATIVE COUNTY

Northamptonshire
Cambridgeshire
BEDFORD DISTRICT
MID-BEDFORDSHIRE DISTRICT
Hertfordshire
SOUTH BEDFORDSHIRE DISTRICT
LUTON
Buckinghamshire
CMD

WATSONIAN VICE-COUNTY 30 BEDFORD

v.c.32 Northampton
v.c.31 Hunts
v.c.29 Cambridge
v.c.24 Bucks
v.c.20 Herts
CMD

THE AREA SURVEYED

A
B
C
D
E
F
M
L
G
K
H
I
J
CMD

THE NATIONAL GRID

SP
TL
96 06 16
95 05 15 25
94 04 14 24
93 03 13 23
92 02 12
91 01 11
CMD

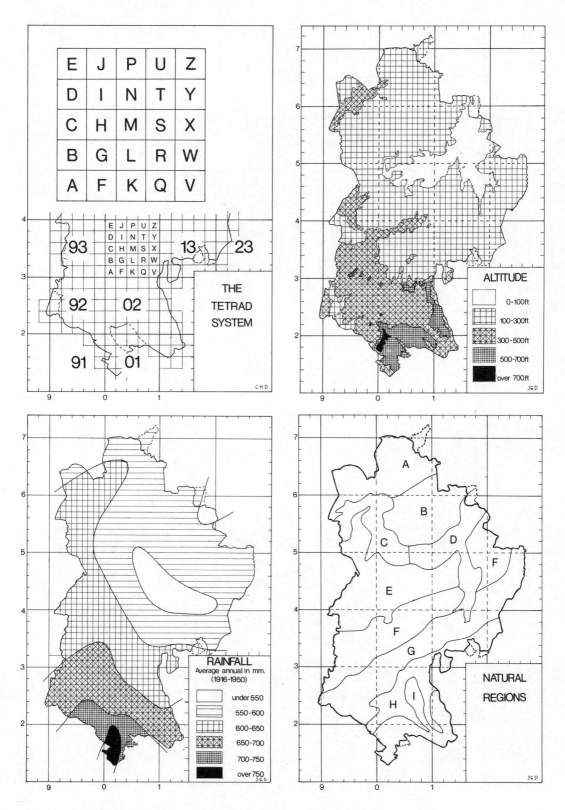

E	J	P	U	Z
D	I	N	T	Y
C	H	M	S	X
B	G	L	R	W
A	F	K	Q	V

93   13   23

92   02

91   01

THE
TETRAD
SYSTEM

CMD

ALTITUDE

0-100ft
100-300ft
300-500ft
500-700ft
over 700ft

JGD

RAINFALL
Average annual in mm.
(1916-1950)

under 550
550-600
600-650
650-700
700-750
over 750

J.G.D.

NATURAL

REGIONS

A
B
C   D
F
E
F
G
H I

JGD

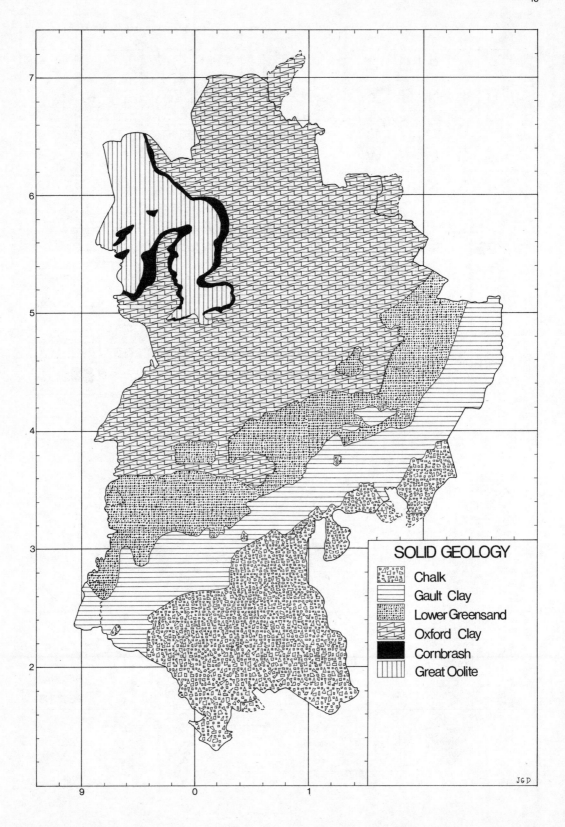

SOLID GEOLOGY

Chalk
Gault Clay
Lower Greensand
Oxford Clay
Cornbrash
Great Oolite

JGD

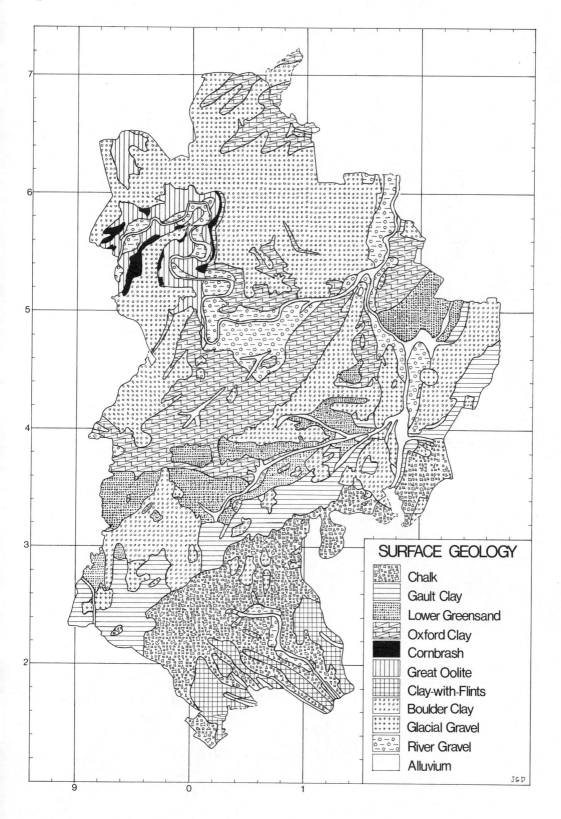

SURFACE GEOLOGY

Chalk
Gault Clay
Lower Greensand
Oxford Clay
Cornbrash
Great Oolite
Clay-with-Flints
Boulder Clay
Glacial Gravel
River Gravel
Alluvium

JGD

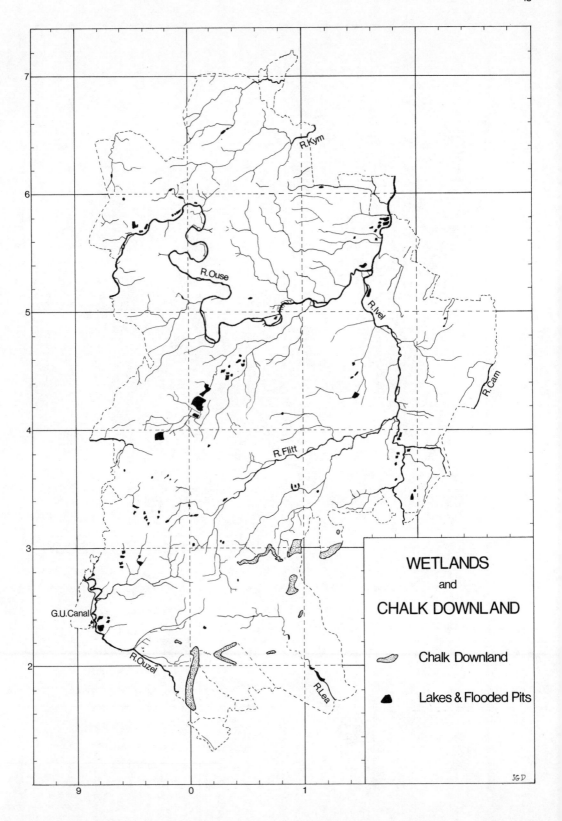

R.Kym

R.Ouse

R.Ivel

R.Cam

R.Flitt

G.U.Canal

R.Ouzel

R.Lea

WETLANDS
and
CHALK DOWNLAND

Chalk Downland

Lakes & Flooded Pits

JGD

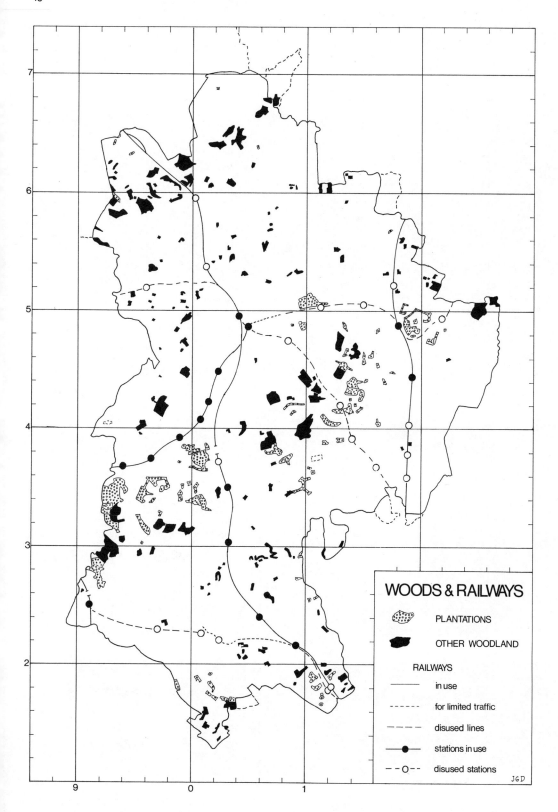

WOODS & RAILWAYS

PLANTATIONS

OTHER WOODLAND

RAILWAYS

in use

for limited traffic

disused lines

stations in use

disused stations

JGD

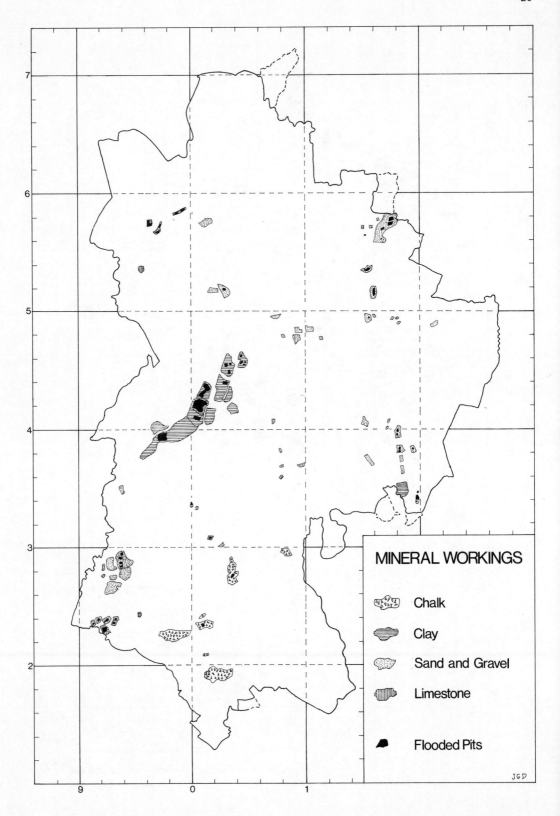

MINERAL WORKINGS

Chalk

Clay

Sand and Gravel

Limestone

Flooded Pits

JGD

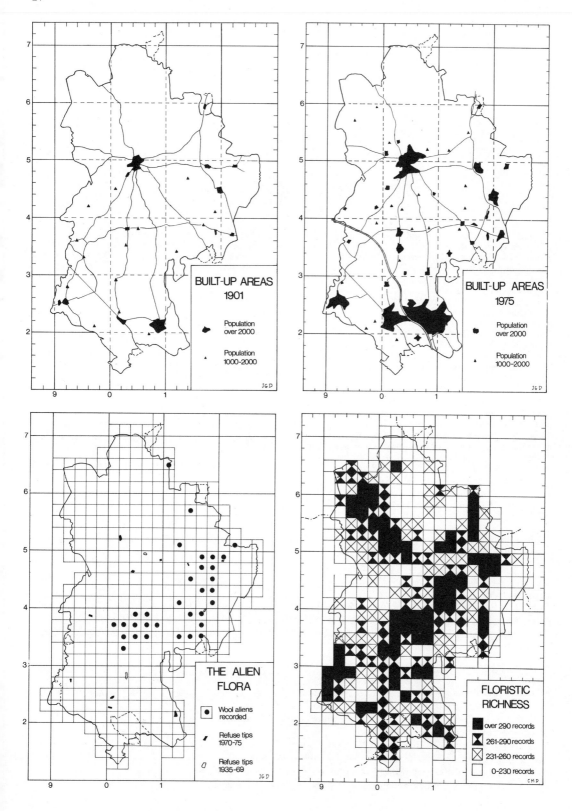

BUILT-UP AREAS
1901

Population
over 2000

Population
1000-2000

JGD

BUILT-UP AREAS
1975

Population
over 2000

Population
1000-2000

JGD

THE ALIEN
FLORA

Wool aliens
recorded

Refuse tips
1970-75

Refuse tips
1935-69

JGD

FLORISTIC
RICHNESS

over 290 records

261-290 records

231-260 records

0-230 records

CMD

The Atlas

The Atlas follows the sequence adopted by Dandy, J. E. (1958). *List of British Vascular Plants*. It brings species closely related to each other together, making comparisons in distribution more readily observed.

The English name, when appropriate, is given priority over the scientific name in the hope that the Atlas may be more readily acceptable to readers who are not botanists. The English names used are those recommended by the Botanical Society of the British Isles in Dony, J. G., F. H. Perring and C. M. Rob (1974). *English Names of Wild Flowers*.

The scientific names mainly follow those used by Dandy, J. E. (1958) except insofar as these are amended by Dandy in *Watsonia* 7, 159–178 (1969). Authors are not given as these are thought to be of interest only to taxonomic botanists.

The habitat given is that in which the species most generally grows in Bedfordshire. Many species may occur occasionally in a large number of other habitats.

Only two symbols are shown on the maps:

● a black dot indicates that the species was found in the tetrad in which the dot is placed at some time in the period of the survey, i.e. 1970–1975 inclusive.

The tetrad to which these dots refer is reduced on the maps to an area about 2·5 times as large as that to which ten-kilometre squares were reduced in the *Atlas of the British Flora* (1962).

○ a hollow circle indicates that the species was known to occur in the tetrad in which the hollow circle is placed at some time in the period 1935–1969 inclusive. It is limited to those species which were found in ten or fewer tetrads during the survey. 1935 is the date when the author began to collect records for the *Flora of Bedfordshire* (1953).

The details of those plants for which maps have not been provided follow the principles adopted in the Atlas for sequence, nomenclature and habitat preferences.

The tetrad numbers which follow some entries indicate that the plant was found in these tetrads at some time in the period of the survey, i.e. 1970–1975 inclusive. Where the tetrad numbers are given in brackets it indicates that the plant was known in these tetrads at some time within the period 1935–1969 inclusive.

‡ indicates that the species is believed to be of garden origin.

* indicates that the species is a casual. This includes bird-seed aliens.

§ indicates a wool alien. The distribution of these species is not given as a map is provided showing where they have occurred.

No indication of status is given for species recorded before 1935 but not since.

All the maps are based upon the Ordnance Survey Map with the sanction of the Controller of Her Majesty's Stationery Office. Crown copyright reserved.

Bibliography

Dony, J. G. (1953). *Flora of Bedfordshire*. This contained a complete bibliography.

Dony, J. G. (1969). Additional Notes on the Flora of Bedfordshire. *Proc. bot. Soc. Br. Isl.* 7, 523–535. This contains a supplementary bibliography and further notes on the flora of the county. Obtainable while stocks last from Luton Museum and Art Gallery, 20p.

Metric Equivalents

1 millimetre (mm.)=0·0394 inch (1 inch=approx. 25 mm.).

1 kilometre (km.)=0·621 (approx. $\frac{5}{8}$) mile (1 mile=approx. 1·6 km.).

10 km.=6·214 (approx. $6\frac{1}{4}$) miles.

1 hectare (10,000 m^2)=2·471 (approx. $2\frac{1}{2}$) acres.

1 sq. kilometre (km.^{2})=100 hectares=0·386 sq. miles=247·1 acres.

4 km.^{2} (i.e. tetrad)=400 hectares=1·744 (approx. $1\frac{3}{4}$) sq. miles=988·4 acres.

100 km.^{2} (i.e. unit of national recording)=38·61 sq. miles=24,710 acres.

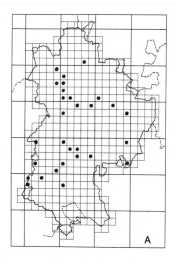

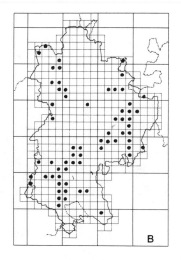

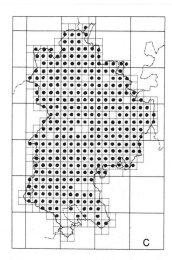

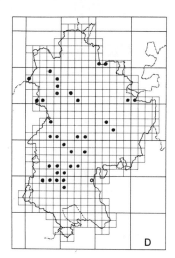

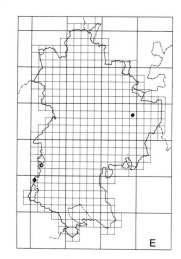

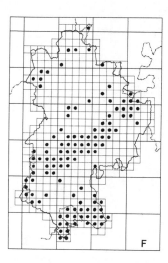

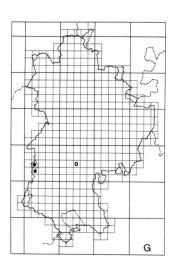

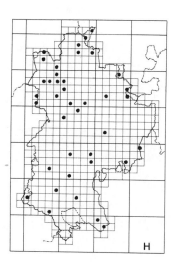

A **Water Horsetail**, *Equisetum fluviatile*. Marshes

B **Marsh Horsetail**, *Equisetum palustre*. Marshes

C **Field Horsetail**, *Equisetum arvense*. Arable fields and waste places

D **Giant Horsetail**, *Equisetum telmateia*. Wet places

E **Royal Fern**, *Osmunda regalis*. Wet places but doubtfully native

F **Bracken**, *Pteridium aquilinum*. Heathy places

G **Hard Fern**, *Blechnum spicant*. Heaths

H **Hart's-tongue**, *Phyllitis scolopendrium*. Walls

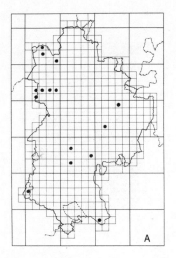

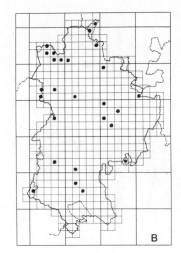

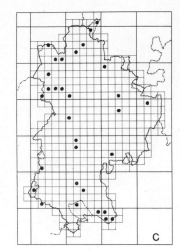

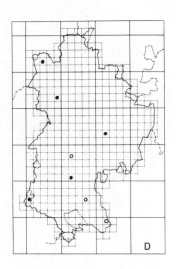

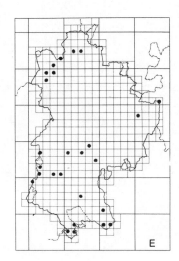

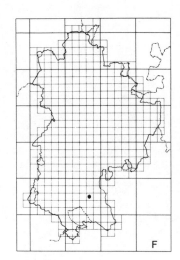

A **Maidenhair Spleenwort**, *Asplenium trichomanes*. Walls

B **Black Spleenwort**, *Asplenium adiantum-nigrum*. Walls

C **Wall-rue**, *Asplenium ruta-muraria*. Walls

D **Rustyback**, *Ceterach officinarum* Walls

E **Lady-fern**, *Athyrium filix-femina*. Woods

F **Brittle Bladder-fern**, *Cystopteris fragilis*. Walls

G **Male-fern**, *Dryopteris filix-mas*. Woods

H **Narrow Buckler-fern**, *Dryopteris carthusiana* (*D. spinulosa*). Woods

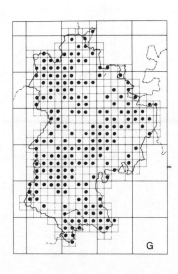

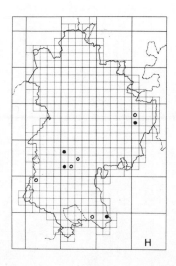

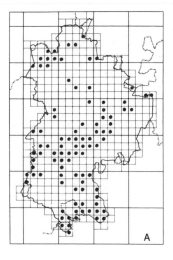

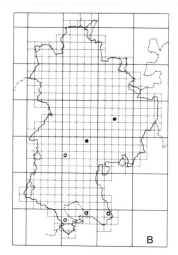

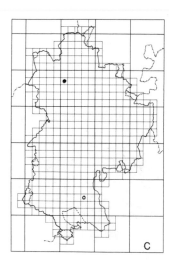

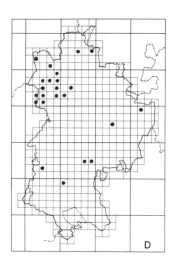

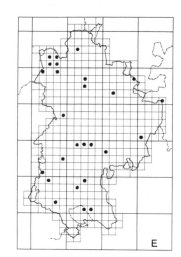

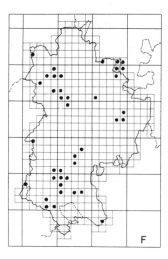

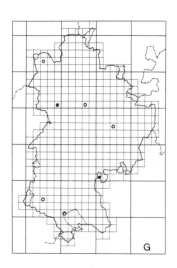

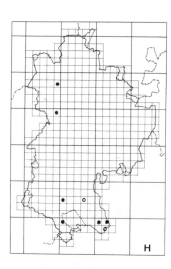

A **Broad Buckler-fern**, *Dryopteris dilatata*. Woods

B **Hard Shield-fern**, *Polystichum aculeatum*. Woods

C **Oak Fern**, *Gymnocarpium dryopteris*. Walls

D **Polypody**, *Polypodium vulgare* subsp. *interjectum*. Walls

E **Adder's-tongue**, *Ophioglossum vulgatum*. Pastures

F **Marsh-marigold**, *Caltha palustris*. Wet places

G **Stinking Hellebore**, *Helleborus foetidus*. Naturalised in hedgerows

H **Green Hellebore**, *Helleborus viridis*. Woods and pastures

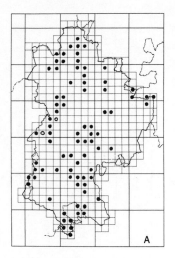

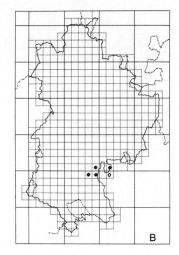

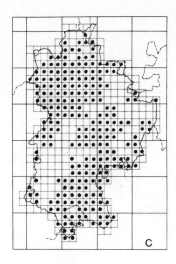

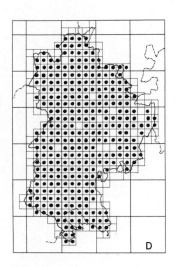

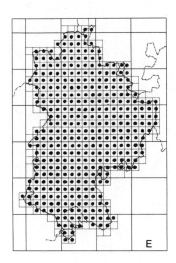

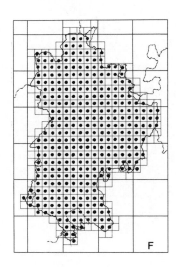

A **Wood Anemone**, *Anemone nemorosa*. Woods

B **Pasqueflower**, *Pulsatilla vulgaris* (*Anemone pulsatilla*). Chalk downland

C **Traveller's-joy**, *Clematis vitalba*. Hedgerows

D **Meadow Buttercup**, *Ranunculus acris*. Pastures

E **Creeping Buttercup**, *Ranunculus repens*. Ubiquitous

F **Bulbous Buttercup**, *Ranunculus bulbosus*. Pastures

G **Corn Buttercup**, *Ranunculus arvensis*. Arable land

H **Hairy Buttercup**, *Ranunculus sardous*. Damp pastures

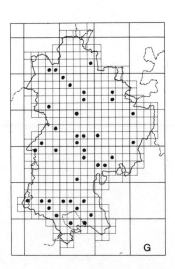

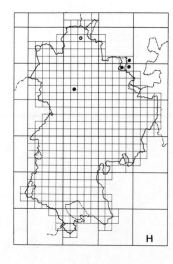

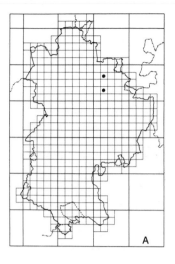

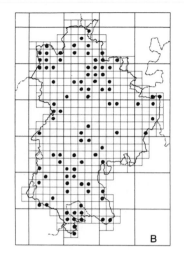

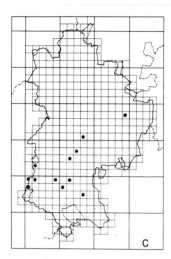

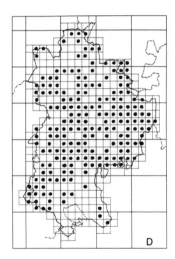

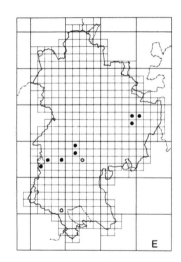

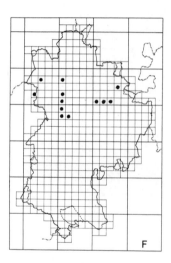

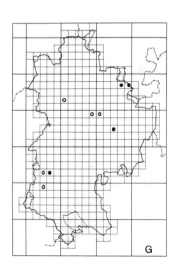

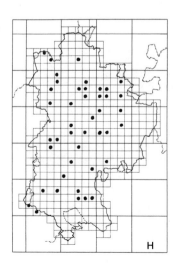

A **Small-flowered Buttercup**, *Ranunculus parviflorus*. Arable land

B **Goldilocks Buttercup**, *Ranunculus auricomus*. Woods

C **Lesser Spearwort**, *Ranunculus flammula*. Wet places

D **Celery-leaved Buttercup**, *Ranunculus sceleratus*. Wet places

E **Ivy-leaved Crowfoot**, *Ranunculus hederaceus*. Wet places

F **River Water-crowfoot**, *Ranunculus fluitans*. Rivers

G **Fan-leaved Water-crowfoot**, *Ranunculus circinatus*. Flooded pits

H **Thread-leaved Water-crowfoot**, *Ranunculus trichophyllus*. Ponds and rivers

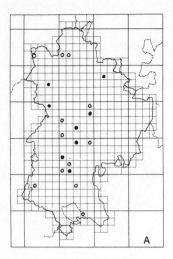

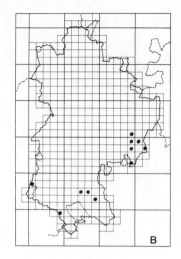

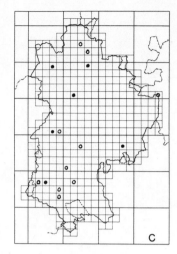

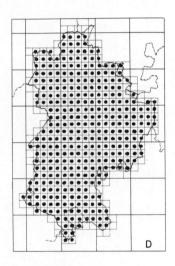

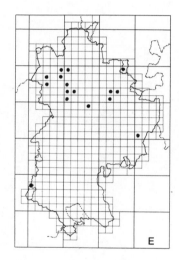

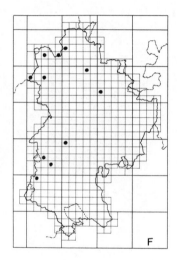

A **Pond Water-crowfoot**, *Ranunculus peltatus*. Ponds

B **Floating Water-crowfoot**, *Ranunculus pseudofluitans*. Chalk streams

C **Common Water-crowfoot**, *Ranunculus aquatilis*. Ponds

D **Lesser Celandine**, *Ranunculus ficaria*. Woods and pastures

E **Common Meadow-rue**, *Thalictrum flavum*. Riversides

F **Barberry**, *Berberis vulgaris*. Hedgerows

G **White Water-lily**, *Nymphaea alba*. Rivers, planted elsewhere

H **Yellow Water-lily**, *Nuphar lutea*. Rivers

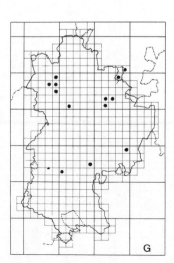

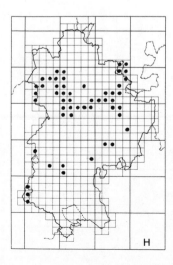

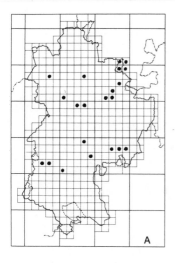

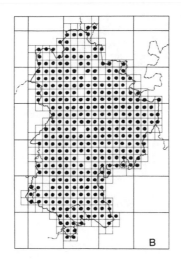

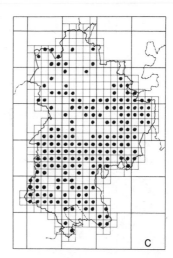

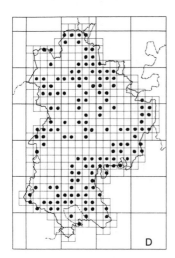

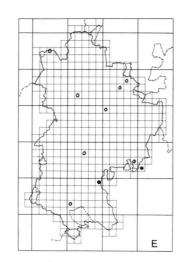

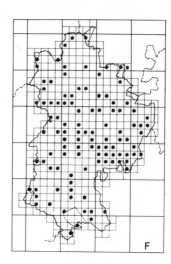

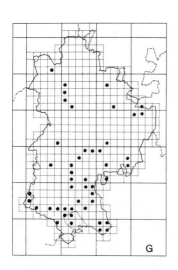

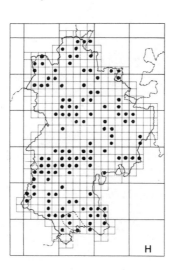

A **Rigid Hornwort**, *Ceratophyllum demersum*. Ponds and rivers

B **Common Poppy**, *Papaver rhoeas*. Arable land and waste places

C **Long-headed Poppy**, *Papaver dubium*. Arable land and waste places

D **Yellow-juiced Poppy**, *Papaver lecoqii*. Arable land and waste places

E **Rough Poppy**, *Papaver hybridum*. Arable land

F **Prickly Poppy**, *Papaver argemone*. Arable fields and railway banks

G **Opium Poppy**, *Papaver somniferum*. Waste places

H **Greater Celandine**, *Chelidonium majus*. Roadsides

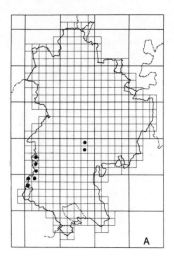

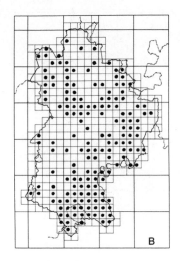

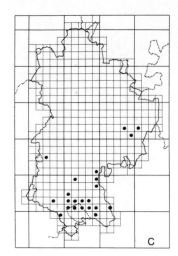

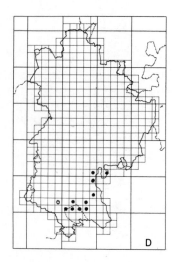

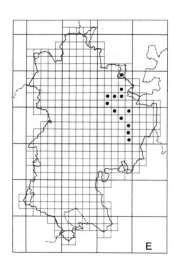

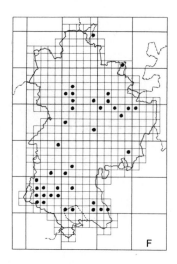

A **Climbing Corydalis**, *Corydalis claviculata*. Woods

B **Common Fumitory**, *Fumaria officinalis*. Arable land and waste places

C **Dense-flowered Fumitory**, *Fumaria densiflora* (*F. micrantha*). Arable land

D **Few-flowered Fumitory**, *Fumaria vaillantii*. Arable land

E **Wild Turnip**, *Brassica rapa*. Riversides

F **Black Mustard**, *Brassica nigra*. Roadsides and waste places

G **Charlock**, *Sinapis arvensis*. Arable land and waste places

H **White Mustard**, *Sinapis alba*. Arable land and waste places

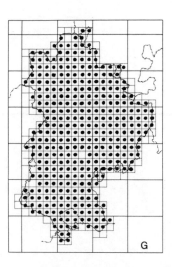

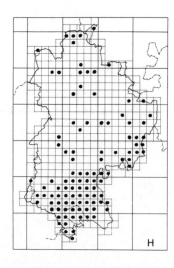

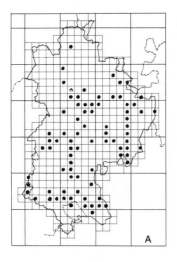

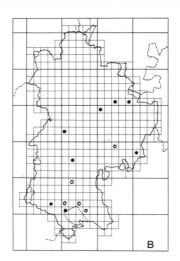

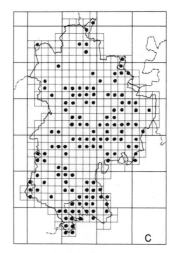

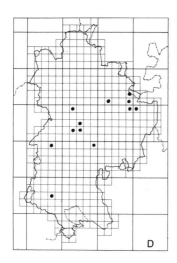

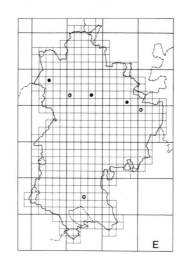

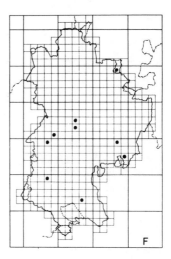

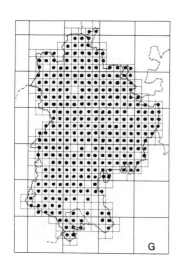

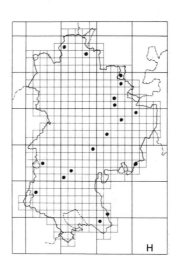

A **Annual Wall-rocket**, *Diplotaxis muralis*. Waste places and railway ballast

B **Perennial Wall-rocket**, *Diplotaxis tenuifolia*. Waste places

C **Wild Radish**, *Raphanus raphanistrum*. Arable land

D **Field Pepperwort**, *Lepidium campestre*. Disturbed ground

E **Smith's Cress**, *Lepidium heterophyllum*. Disturbed ground

F **Narrow-leaved Pepperwort**, *Lepidium ruderale*. Waste places

G **Swine-cress**, *Coronopus squamatus*. Arable land

H **Lesser Swine-cress**, *Coronopus didymus*. Waste places

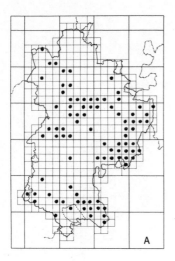

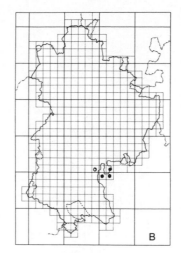

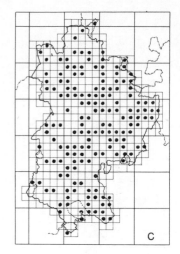

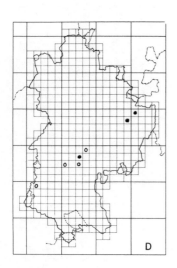

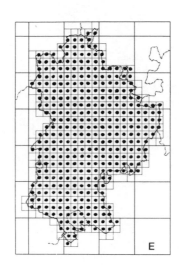

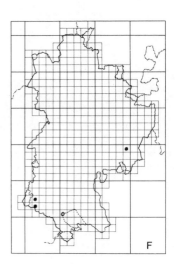

A **Hoary Cress**, *Cardaria draba*. Arable land and waste places

B **Wild Candytuft**, *Iberis amara*. Field borders

C **Field Penny-cress**, *Thlaspi arvense*. Arable land

D **Shepherd's Cress**, *Teesdalia nudicaulis*. Sandy banks

E **Shepherd's-purse**, *Capsella bursa-pastoris*. Arable land

F **Wall Whitlowgrass**, *Draba muralis*. Bare ground

G **Common Whitlowgrass**, *Erophila verna*. Bare ground

H **Horse-radish**, *Armoracia rusticana*. Waste places

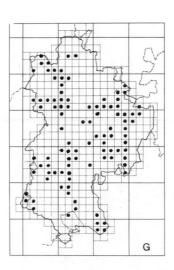

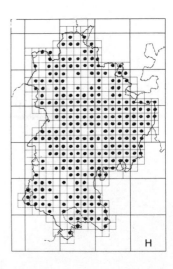

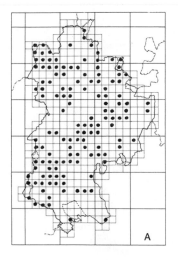

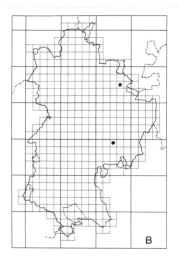

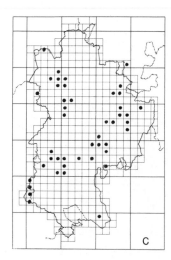

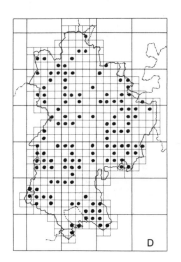

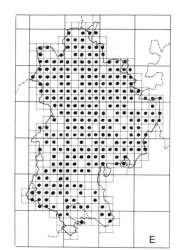

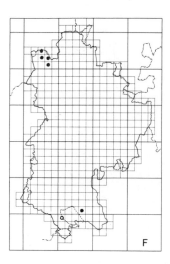

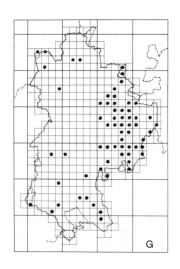

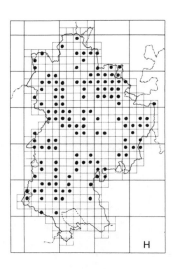

A **Cuckooflower**, *Cardamine pratensis*. Meadows

B **Large Bitter-cress**, *Cardamine amara*. Riversides

C **Wavy Bitter-cress**, *Cardamine flexuosa*. Damp shady places

D **Hairy Bitter-cress**, *Cardamine hirsuta*. Bare ground

E **Winter-cress**, *Barbarea vulgaris*. Roadsides and ditches.

F **Hairy Rock-cress**, *Arabis hirsuta*. Dry banks

G **Water-cress*** *Rorippa nasturtium-aquaticum*. Rivers

H **Water-cress***, *Rorippa microphylla*. Rivers and ditches

* These species do not merit separate English names.

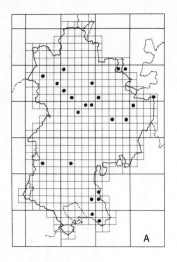

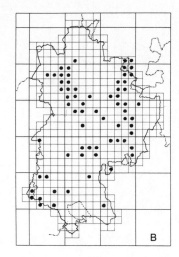

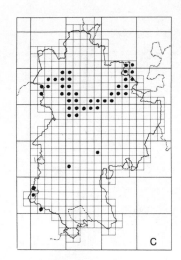

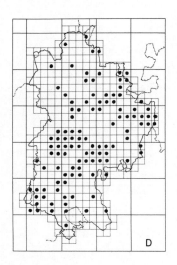

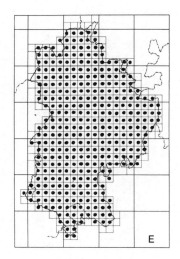

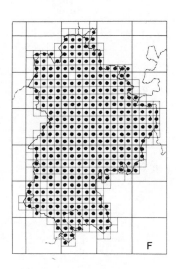

A **Creeping Yellow-cress**, *Rorippa sylvestris*. Wet places and gardens

B **Marsh Yellow-cress**, *Rorippa islandica*. Wet and waste places

C **Great Yellow-cress**, *Rorippa amphibia*. Riversides

D **Treacle Mustard**, *Erysimum cheiranthoides*. Arable land

E **Garlic Mustard**, *Alliaria petiolata*. Hedgerows

F **Hedge Mustard**, *Sisymbrium officinale*. Waste places

G **Eastern Rocket**, *Sisymbrium orientale*. Waste places

H **Tall Rocket**, *Sisymbrium altissimum*. Waste places

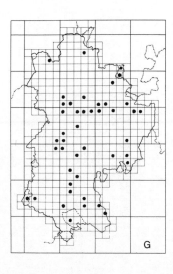

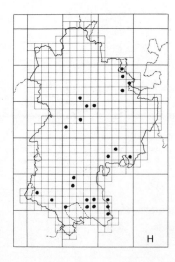

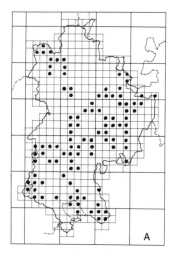

A

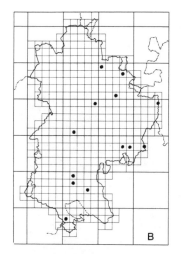

B

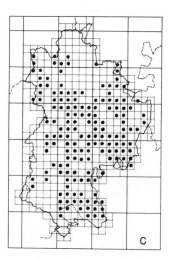

C

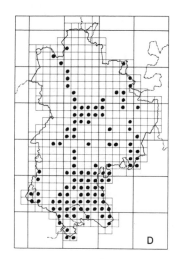

D

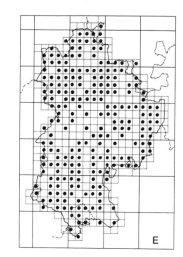

E

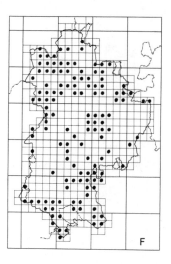

F

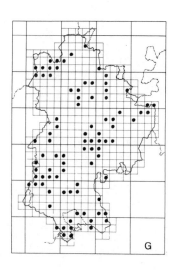

G

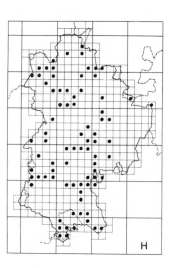

H

A **Thale Cress**, *Arabidopsis thaliana*.
Bare ground

B **Flixweed**, *Descurania sophia*. Waste
places

C **Weld**, *Reseda luteola*. Rough pastures

D **Wild Mignonette**, *Reseda lutea*.
Chalk downland

E **Sweet Violet**, *Viola odorata*. Hedgebanks

F **Hairy Violet**, *Viola hirta* subsp. *hirta*.
Calcareous pastures

G **Common Dog-violet**, *Viola riviniana*.
Woods

H **Early Dog-violet**, *Viola reichen-
bachiana*. Woods

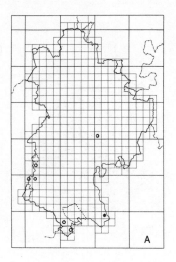

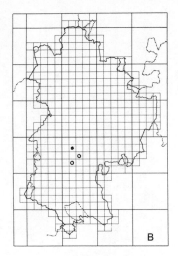

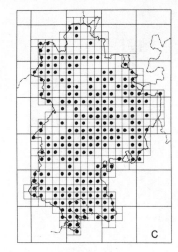

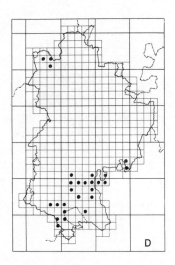

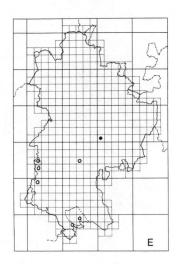

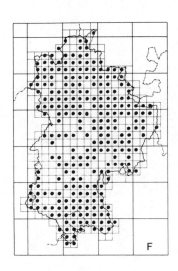

A **Heath Dog-violet**, *Viola canina*. Heaths

B **Marsh Violet**, *Viola palustris*. Marshes

C **Field Pansy**, *Viola arvensis*. Arable land

D **Common Milkwort**, *Polygala vulgaris* (including *P. oxyptera*). Calcareous pastures

E **Heath Milkwort**, *Polygala serpyllifolia*. Heaths

F **Perforate St. John's-wort**, *Hypericum perforatum*. Hedgebanks

G **Imperforate St. John's-wort**, *Hypericum maculatum* subsp. *obtusiusculum* (*H. dubium*). Hedgebanks

H **Square-stalked St. John's-wort**, *Hypericum tetrapterum*. Wet places

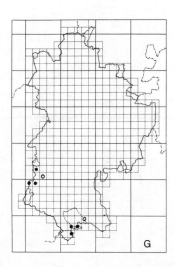

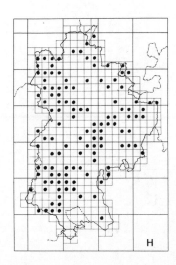

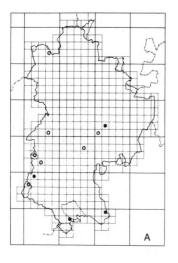

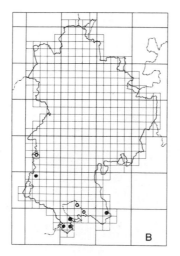

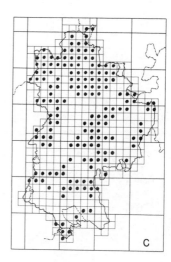

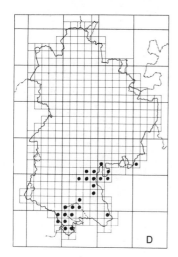

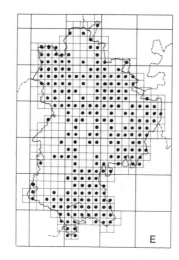

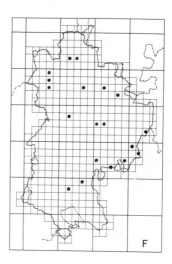

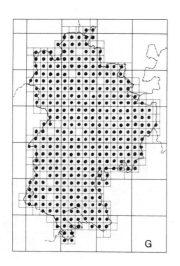

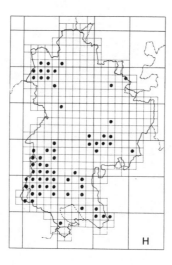

A **Trailing St. John's-wort**, *Hypericum humifusum*. Heaths

B **Slender St. John's-wort**, *Hypericum pulchrum*. Woodland rides

C **Hairy St. John's-wort**, *Hypericum hirsutum*. Woods and hedgebanks

D **Common Rock-rose**, *Helianthemum chamaecistus*. Chalk downland

E **Bladder Campion**, *Silene vulgaris*. Waste places

F **Night-flowering Catchfly**, *Silene noctiflora* (*Melandrium noctiflorum*). Arable land

G **White Campion**, *Silene alba* (*Melandrium album*). Waste places

H **Red Campion**, *Silene dioica* (*Melandrium dioicum*). Roadsides and wood borders

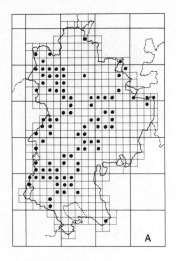

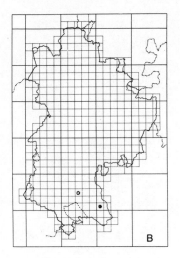

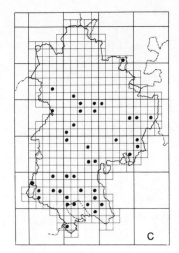

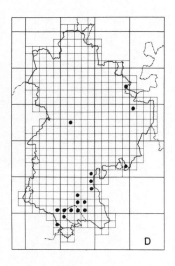

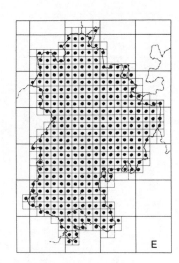

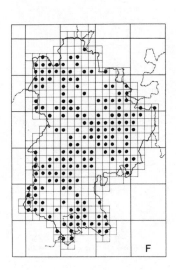

A **Ragged-Robin**, *Lychnis flos-cuculi.* Wet places

B **Deptford Pink**, *Dianthus armeria.* Dry banks

C **Soapwort**, *Saponaria officinalis.* Roadsides

D **Field Mouse-ear**, *Cerastium arvense.* Disturbed soils

E **Common Mouse-ear**, *Cerastium holosteoides.* Pastures

F **Sticky Mouse-ear**, *Cerastium glomeratum.* Dry banks and pastures

G **Grey Mouse-ear**, *Cerastium brachypetalum.* Railway banks

H **Sea Mouse-ear**, *Cerastium diffusum* (*C. tetrandrum*). Railway ballast

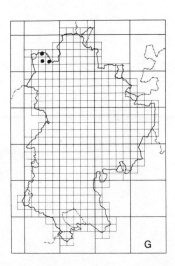

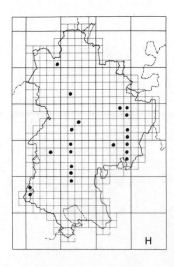

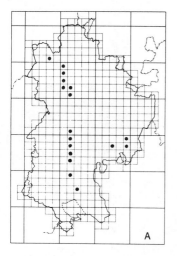

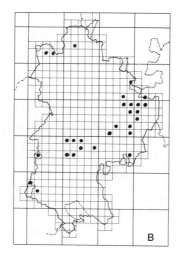

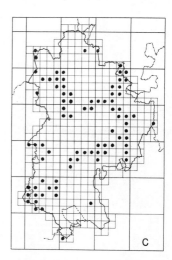

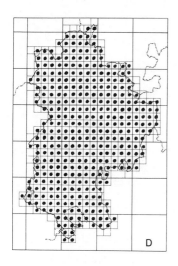

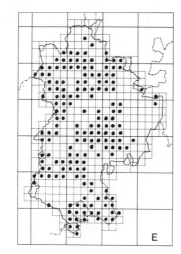

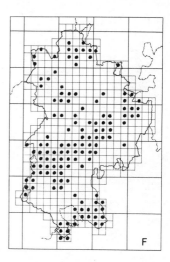

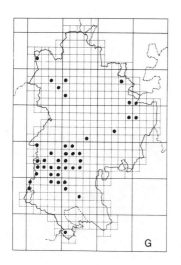

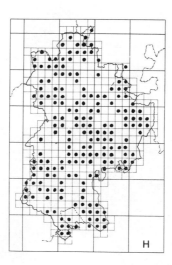

A **Dwarf Mouse-ear**, *Cerastium pumilum*. Railway banks

B **Little Mouse-ear**, *Cerastium semidecandrum*. Dry banks

C **Water Chickweed**, *Myosoton aquaticum*. Wet places

D **Common Chickweed**, *Stellaria media*. Arable land and waste places

E **Greater Stitchwort**, *Stellaria holostea*. Hedgerows and wood borders

F **Lesser Stitchwort**, *Stellaria graminea*. Heaths

G **Bog Stitchwort**, *Stellaria alsine*. Wet places

H **Procumbent Pearlwort**, *Sagina procumbens*. Pastures and bare ground

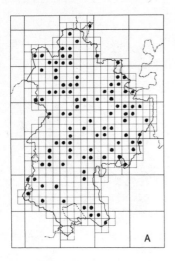

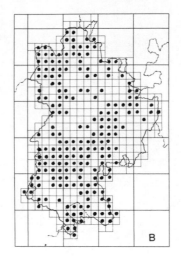

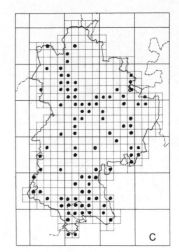

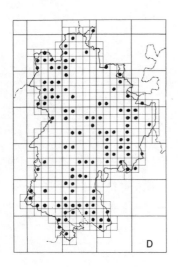

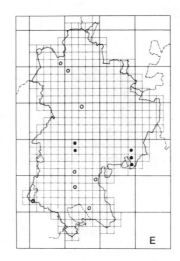

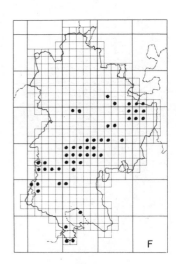

A **Annual Pearlwort**, *Sagina apetala* (including *S. ciliata*). Bare ground

B **Three-nerved Sandwort**, *Moehringia trinervia*. Woods

C **Thyme-leaved Sandwort**, *Arenaria serpyllifolia*. Dry banks and bare ground

D **Slender Sandwort**, *Arenaria leptoclados*. Dry banks and bare ground

E **Fine-leaved Sandwort**, *Minuartia hybrida*. (*M. tenuifolia*). Bare ground

F **Corn Spurrey**, *Spergula arvensis*. Arable land

G **Sand Spurrey**, *Spergularia rubra*, Heaths

H **Annual Knawel**, *Scleranthus annuus*. Arable land

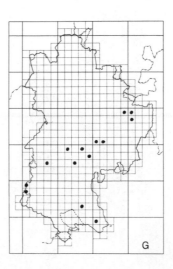

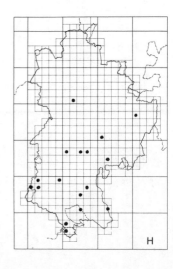

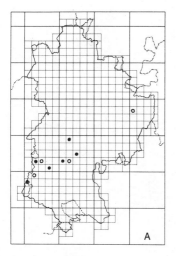

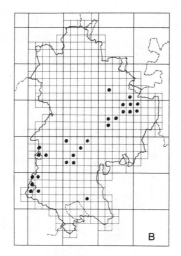

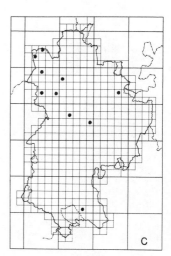

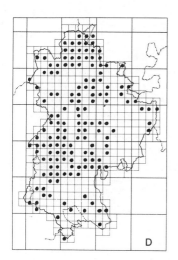

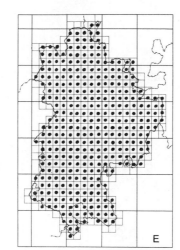

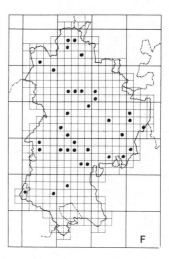

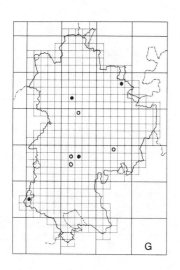

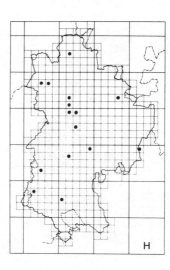

A **Blinks**, *Montia fontana*. Wet places

B **Springbeauty**, *Montia perfoliata* (*Claytonia p.*). Bare sandy ground

C **Good-King-Henry**, *Chenopodium bonus-henricus*. Waste ground near old houses

D **Many-seeded Goosefoot**, *Chenopodium polyspermum*. Arable land

E **Fat-hen**, *Chenopodium album*. Arable land and waste places

F **Fig-leaved Goosefoot**, *Chenopodium ficifolium*. Arable land

G **Nettle-leaved Goosefoot**, *Chenopodium murale*. Arable land and waste ground

H **Maple-leaved Goosefoot**, *Chenopodium hybridum*. Arable land

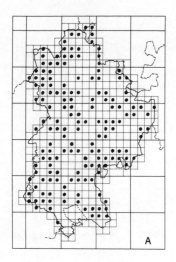

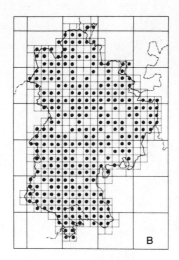

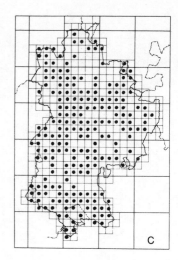

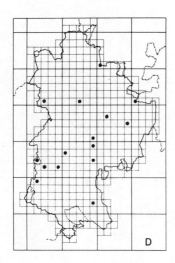

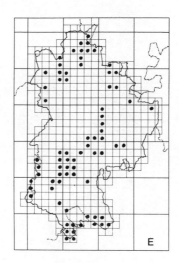

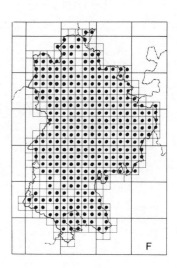

A **Red Goosefoot**, *Chenopodium rubrum*. Waste places and farmland

B **Common Orache**, *Atriplex patula*. Roadsides and arable land

C **Spear-leaved Orache**, *Atriplex hastata*. Waste places and farmland

D **Small-leaved Lime**, *Tilia cordata*. Native in woods, planted elsewhere

E **Musk Mallow**, *Malva moschata*. Hedgerows

F **Common Mallow**, *Malva sylvestris*. Roadsides and waste places

G **Dwarf Mallow**, *Malva neglecta*. Roadsides

H **Fairy Flax**, *Linum catharticum*. Calcareous pastures

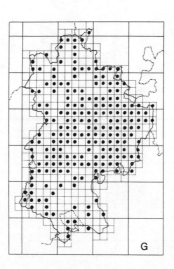

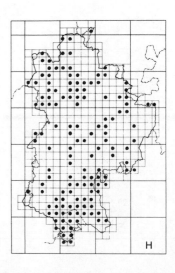

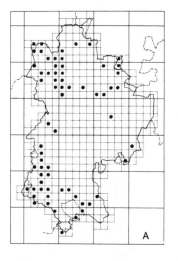

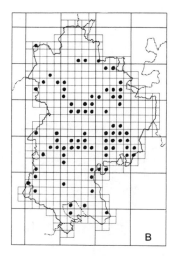

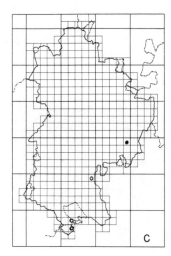

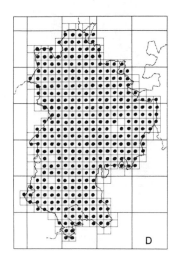

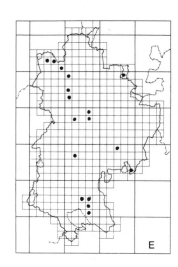

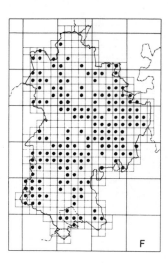

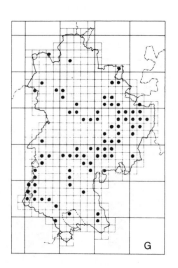

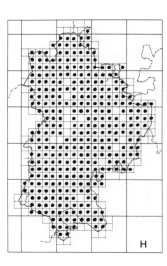

A **Meadow Crane's-bill**, *Geranium pratense*. Pastures

B **Hedgerow Crane's-bill**, *Geranium pyrenaicum*. Roadsides

C **Long-stalked Crane's-bill**, *Geranium columbinum*. Dry banks

D **Cut-leaved Crane's-bill**, *Geranium dissectum*. Arable land and waste places

E **Round-leaved Crane's-bill**, *Geranium rotundifolium*. Railway banks and waste land

F **Dove's-foot Crane's-bill**, *Geranium molle*. Pastures and waste places

G **Small-flowered Crane's-bill**, *Geranium pusillum*. Pastures and waste places

H **Herb-Robert**, *Geranium robertianum*. Hedgerows and wood borders

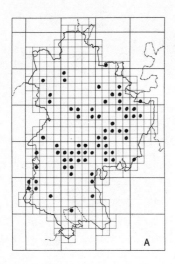

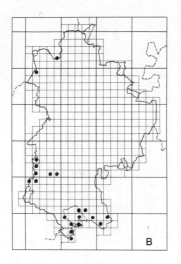

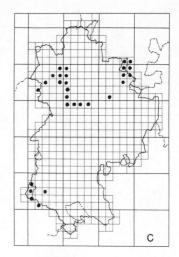

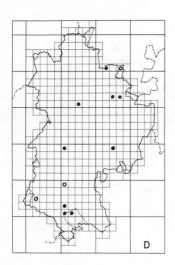

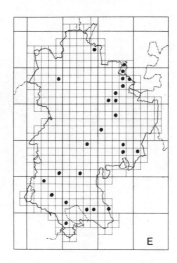

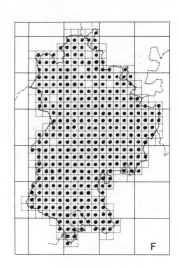

A **Common Stork's-bill**, *Erodium cicu-tarium*. Sandy fields occurring also as a wool alien

B **Wood-sorrel**, *Oxalis acetosella*. Woods

C **Orange Balsam**, *Impatiens capensis*. Riversides

D **Small Balsam**, *Impatiens parviflora*. Waste places

E **Indian Balsam**, *Impatiens glandu-lifera*. Riversides and waste places

F **Sycamore**, *Acer pseudoplatanus*. Woods

G **Field Maple**, *Acer campestre*. Woods and hedgerows

H **Holly**, *Ilex aquifolium*. Woods and hedgerows

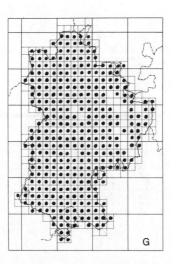

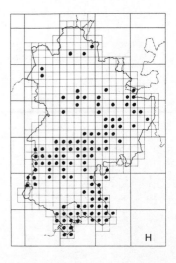

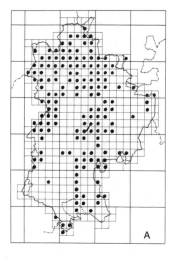

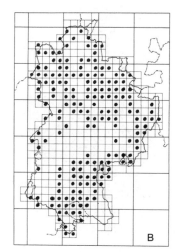

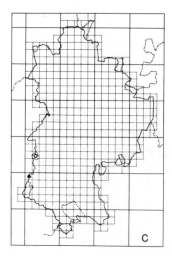

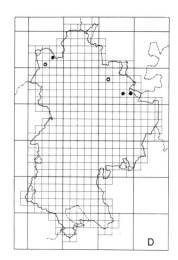

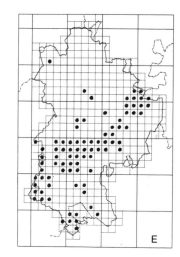

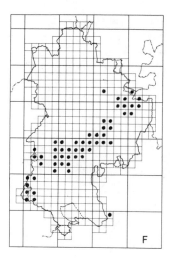

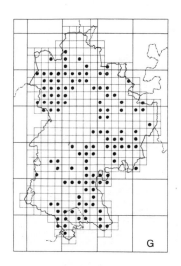

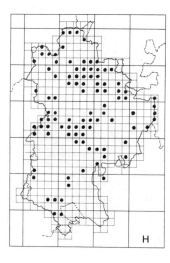

A **Spindle**, *Euonymus europaeus*. Hedgerows

B **Buckthorn**, *Rhamnus catharticus*.
Hedgerows

C **Alder Buckthorn**, *Frangula alnus*.
Woods

D **Dyer's Greenweed**, *Genista tinctoria*.
Pastures

E **Gorse**, *Ulex europaeus*. Heaths

F **Broom**, *Sarothamnus scoparius*. Heaths

G **Common Restharrow**, *Ononis repens*.
Pastures

H **Spiny Restharrow**, *Ononis spinosa*.
Pastures

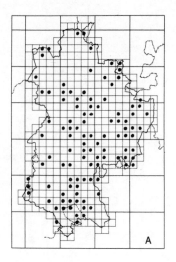

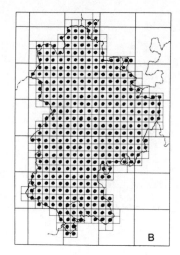

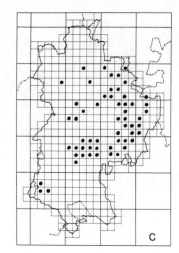

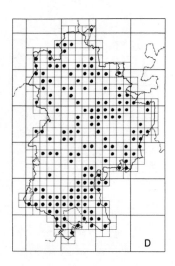

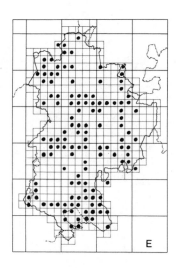

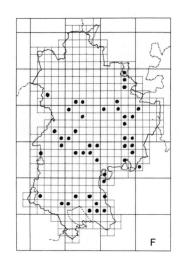

A **Lucerne**, *Medicago sativa*. Pastures

B **Black Medick**, *Medicago lupulina*. Pastures and waste places

C **Spotted Medick**, *Medicago arabica*. Sandy pastures occurring also as a wool alien

D **Tall Melilot**, *Melilotus altissima*. Pastures and waste places

E **Ribbed Melilot**. *Melilotus officinalis*. Pastures and waste places

F **White Melilot**, *Melilotus alba*. Waste places

G **Red Clover**, *Trifolium pratense*. Pastures

H **Sulphur Clover**, *Trifolium ochroleucon*. Roadside verges

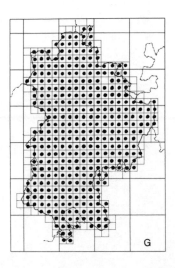

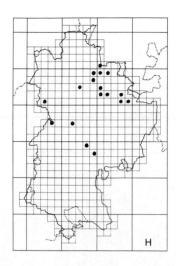

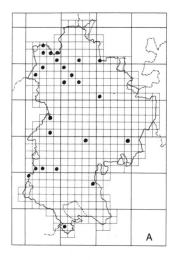

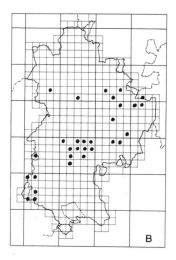

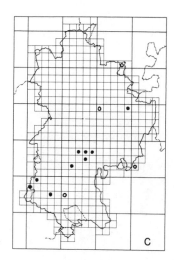

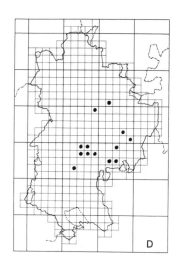

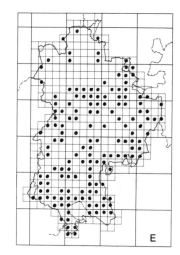

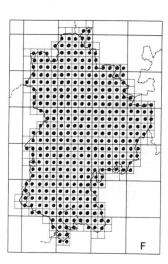

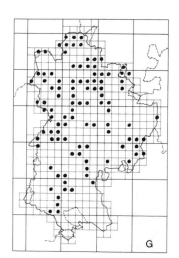

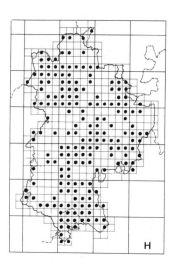

A **Zigzag Clover**, *Trifolium medium.* Pastures and railway banks

B **Hare's-foot Clover**, *Trifolium arvense.* Sandy pastures

C **Knotted Clover**, *Trifolium striatum.* Sandy pastures

D **Subterranean Clover**, *Trifolium subterraneum.* Sandy pastures occurring also as a wool alien

E **Alsike Clover**, *Trifolium hybridum.* Pastures and relic of cultivation

F **White Clover**, *Trifolium repens.* Pastures and waste places

G **Strawberry Clover**, *Trifolium fragiferum.* Pastures

H **Hop Trefoil**, *Trifolium campestre.* Pastures

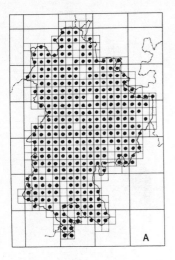

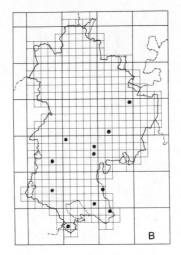

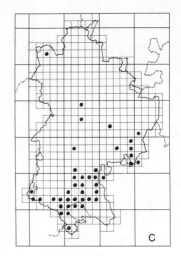

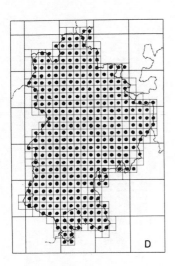

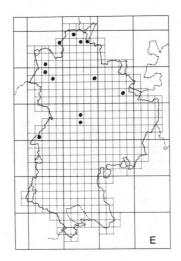

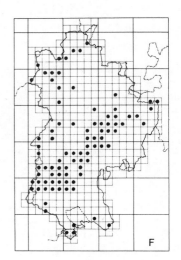

A **Lesser Trefoil**, *Trifolium dubium*. Pastures and hedgebanks

B **Slender Trefoil**, *Trifolium micranthum*. Pastures

C **Kidney Vetch**, *Anthyllis vulneraria*. Calcareous pastures

D **Common Bird's-foot-trefoil**, *Lotus corniculatus*. Pastures

E **Narrow-leaved Bird's-foot-trefoil**, *Lotus tenuis*. Pastures

F **Greater Bird's-foot-trefoil**, *Lotus uliginosus*. Woods and marshes

G **Goat's-rue**, *Galega officinalis*. Waste places

H **Bladder-senna**, *Colutea arborescens*. Railway banks

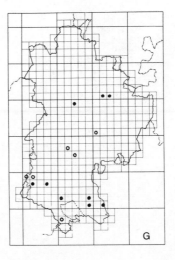

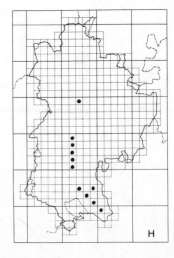

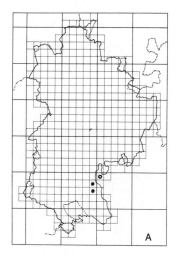

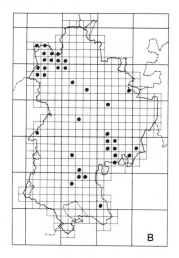

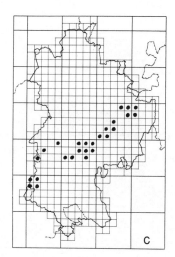

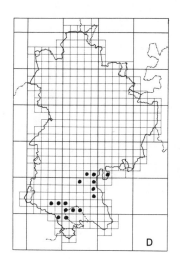

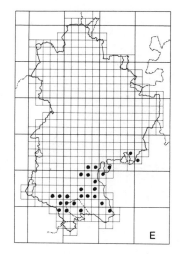

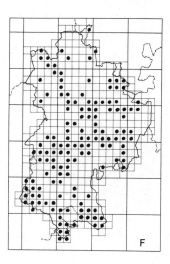

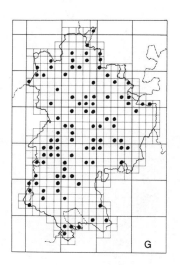

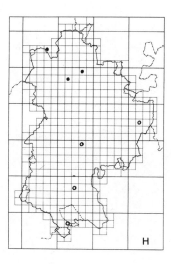

A **Purple Milk-vetch**, *Astragalus danicus*. Chalk downland

B **Wild Liquorice**, *Astragalus glycyphyllus*. Hedgebanks and scrub

C **Bird's-foot**, *Ornithopus perpusillus*. Sandy pastures

D **Horseshoe Vetch**, *Hippocrepis comosa*. Chalk downland

E **Sainfoin**, *Onobrychis viciifolia*. Chalk downland

F **Hairy Tare**, *Vicia hirsuta*. Hedgebanks

G **Smooth Tare**, *Vicia tetrasperma*. Hedgebanks

H **Slender Tare**, *Vicia tenuissima*. Hedgebanks

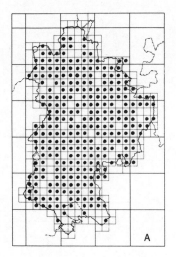

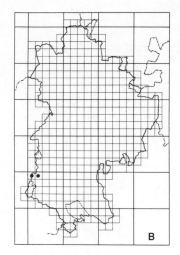

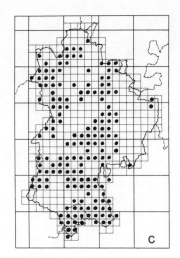

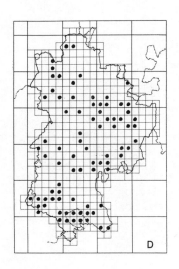

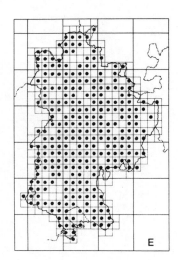

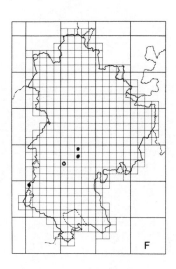

A **Tufted Vetch**, *Vicia cracca*. Hedge banks and wood borders

B **Wood Vetch**, *Vicia sylvatica*. Woods

C **Bush Vetch**, *Vicia sepium*. Woods and hedgerows

D **Common Vetch**, *Vicia sativa*. Mainly a relic of cultivation

E **Narrow-leaved Vetch**, *Vicia angustifolia*. Pastures

F **Spring Vetch**, *Vicia lathyroides*. Sandy pastures

G **Grass Vetchling**, *Lathyrus nissolia*. Pastures

H **Meadow Vetchling**, *Lathyrus pratensis*. Pastures

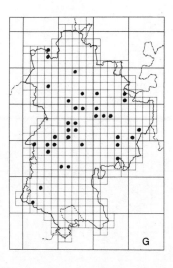

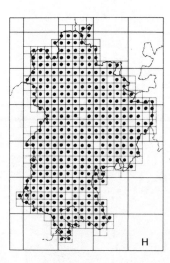

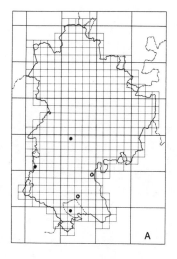

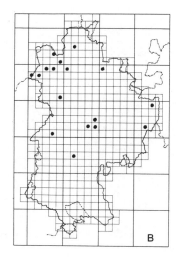

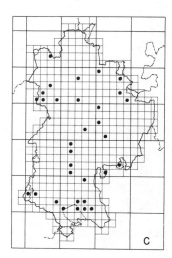

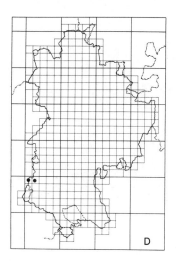

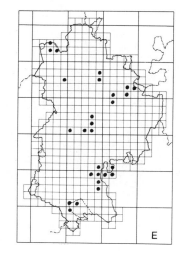

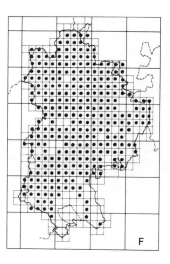

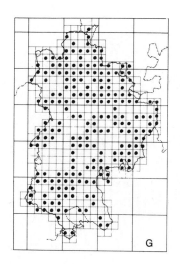

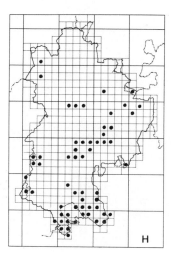

A **Tuberous Pea**, *Lathyrus tuberosus*. Rough grassland

B **Narrow-leaved Everlasting-pea**, *Lathyrus sylvestris*. Wood borders and railway banks

C **Broad-leaved Everlasting-pea**, *Lathyrus latifolius*. Waste places

D **Bitter Vetch**, *Lathyrus montanus*. Woods

E **Dropwort**, *Filipendula vulgaris*. Calcareous pastures

F **Meadowsweet**, *Filipendula ulmaria*. Wet places

G **Dewberry**, *Rubus caesius*. Hedgerows

H **Raspberry**, *Rubus idaeus*. Heaths and woods

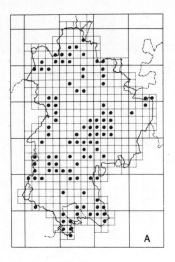

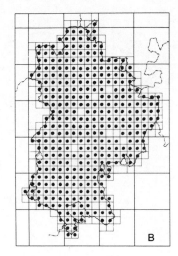

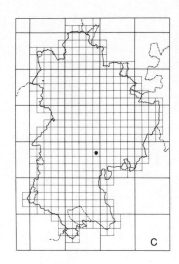

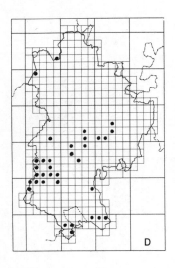

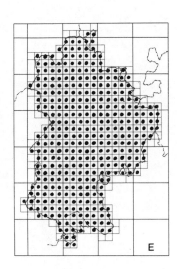

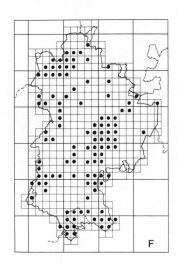

A **Barren Strawberry**, *Potentilla sterilis*. Woods and hedgebanks

B **Silverweed**, *Potentilla anserina*. Roadsides and waste places

C **Hoary Cinquefoil**, *Potentilla argentea*. Sandy pastures

D **Tormentil**, *Potentilla erecta*. Heaths

E **Creeping Cinquefoil**, *Potentilla reptans*. Pastures and waste ground

F **Wild Strawberry**, *Fragaria vesca*. Hedgebanks and woodland rides

G **Garden Strawberry**, *Fragaria ananassa*. Railway banks

H **Wood Avens**, *Geum urbanum*. Woods and hedgerows

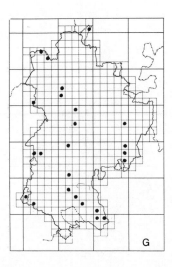

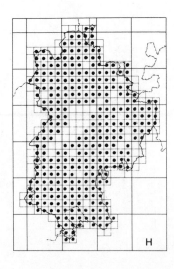

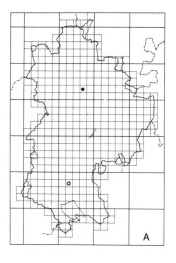

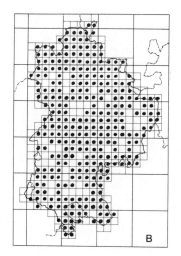

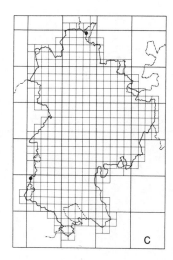

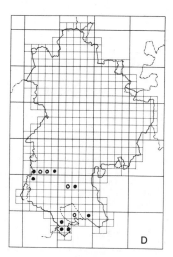

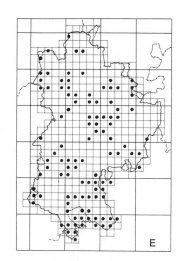

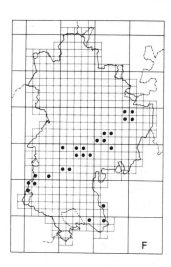

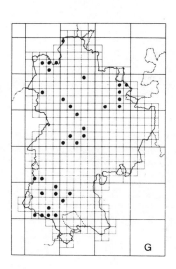

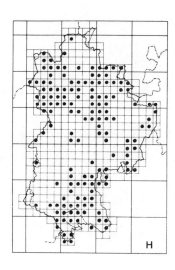

A **Water Avens**, *Geum rivale*. Woods

B **Agrimony**, *Agrimonia eupatoria*. Pastures

C **Fragrant Agrimony**, *Agrimonia odorata*. Rough pastures

D **Lady's-mantle**, *Alchemilla vestita*. Pastures and woodland rides

E **Parsley-piert**, *Aphanes arvensis*. Arable land

F **Slender Parsley-piert**, *Aphanes microcarpa*. Bare sandy ground

G **Great Burnet**, *Sanguisorba officinalis*. Pastures

H **Salad Burnet**, *Poterium sanguisorba*. Calcareous pastures

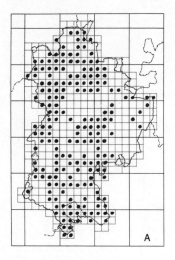

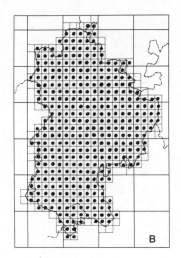

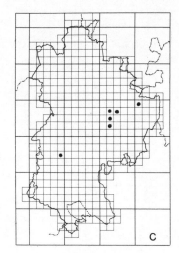

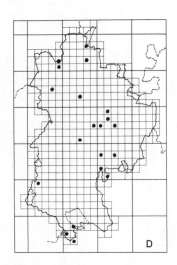

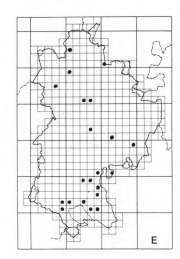

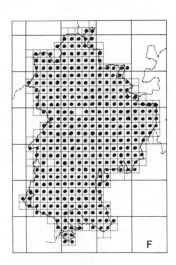

A **Field Rose**, *Rosa arvensis*. Hedgerows

B **Dog Rose**, *Rosa canina*. Hedgerows and scrub

C **Sweet Briar**, *Rosa rubiginosa*. Scrub

D **Downy Rose**, *Rosa tomentosa*. Hedgerows

E *Rosa stylosa*. Hedgerows

F **Blackthorn**, *Prunus spinosa*. Hedgerows

G **Cherry Plum**, *Prunus cerasifera*. Hedgerows

H **Wild Cherry**, *Prunus avium*. Woods

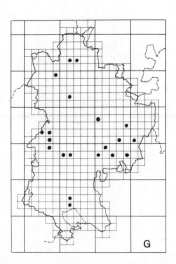

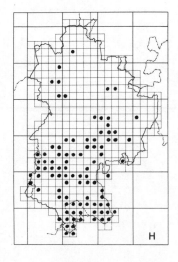

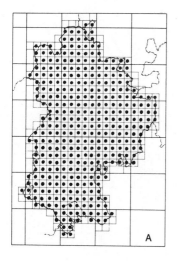

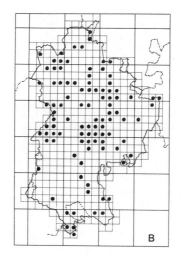

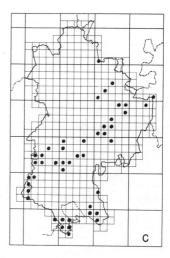

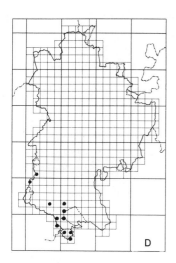

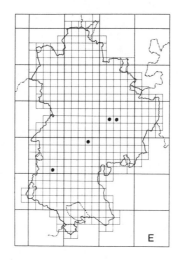

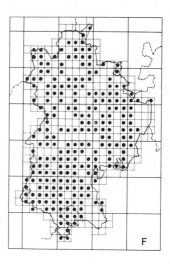

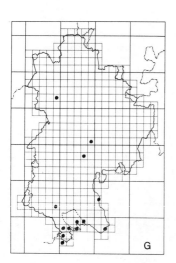

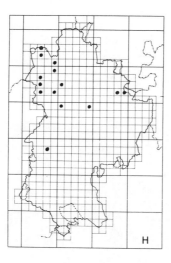

A **Hawthorn**, *Crataegus monogyna.*
Hedgerows and scrub

B **Midland Hawthorn**, *Crataegus laevigata (C. oxyacanthoides)*. Woods and hedgerows

C **Rowan**, *Sorbus aucuparia.* Woods

D **Common Whitebeam**, *Sorbus aria.*
Wood borders

E **Wild Service-tree**, *Sorbus torminalis.*
Woods

F **Crab Apple**, *Malus sylvestris.* Hedgerows

G **Orpine**, *Sedum telephium.* Wood borders

H **White Stonecrop**, *Sedum album.*
Walls

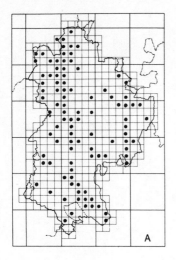

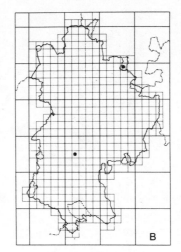

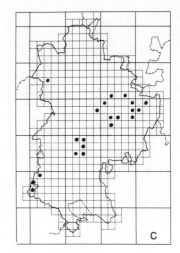

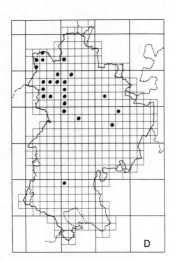

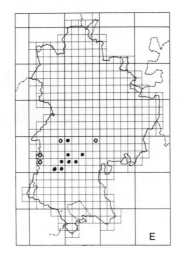

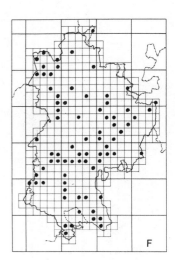

A **Biting Stonecrop**, *Sedum acre*. Bare ground

B **Thick-leaved Stonecrop**, *Sedum dasyphyllum*. Walls

C **Meadow Saxifrage**, *Saxifraga granulata*. Pastures

D **Rue-leaved Saxifrage**, *Saxifraga tridactylites*. Walls and bare ground

E **Opposite-leaved Golden-saxifrage**, *Chrysosplenium oppositifolium*. Wet shady places

F **Red Currant**, *Ribes rubrum (R. sylvestre)*. Woods

G **Black Currant**, *Ribes nigrum*. Riversides and wet woods

H **Gooseberry**, *Ribes uva-crispa*. Hedgerows

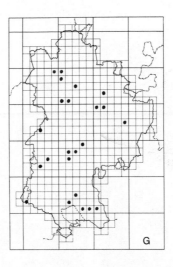

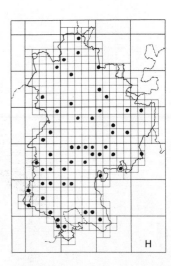

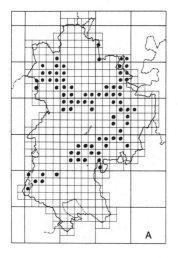

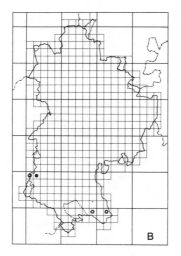

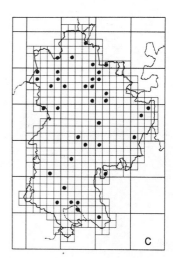

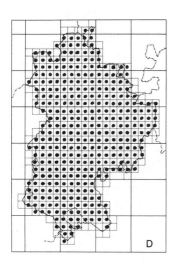

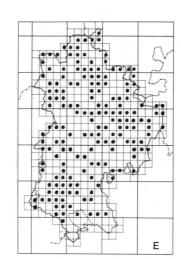

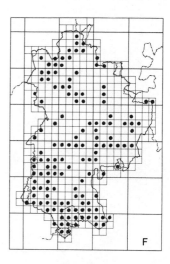

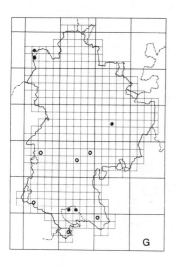

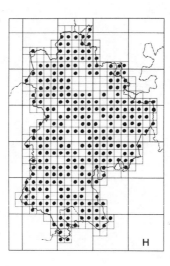

A **Purple-loosestrife**, *Lythrum salicaria*. Riversides

B **Water-purslane**, *Peplis portula*. Wet places

C **Spurge-laurel**, *Daphne laureola*. Woods and hedgerows

D **Great Willowherb**, *Epilobium hirsutum*. Wet places

E **Hoary Willowherb**, *Epilobium parviflorum*. Wet places

F **Broad-leaved Willowherb**, *Epilobium montanum*. Woods

G **Pale Willowherb**, *Epilobium roseum*. Waste places

H **American Willowherb**, *Epilobium adenocaulon*. Woods and waste places

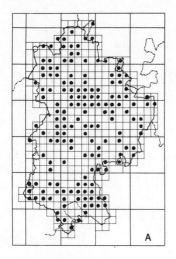

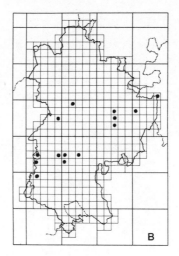

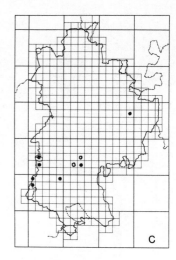

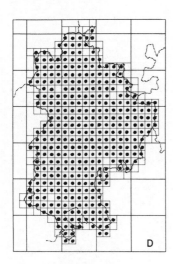

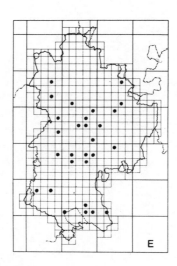

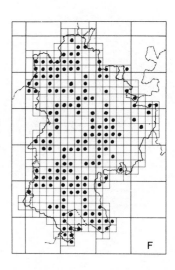

A **Square-stalked Willowherb**, *Epilobium tetragonum* (including *E. lamyi*). Waste places

B **Short-fruited Willowherb**, *Epilobium obscurum*. Woods

C **Marsh Willowherb**, *Epilobium palustre*. Marshes

D **Rosebay Willowherb**, *Epilobium angustifolium* (*Chamaenerion a.*). Woods and waste places

E **Large-flowered Evening-primrose**, *Oenothera erythrosepala*. Waste places

F **Enchanter's-nightshade**, *Circaea lutetiana*. Woods

G **Spiked Water-milfoil**, *Myriophyllum spicatum*. Rivers, lakes and flooded pits

H **Whorled Water-milfoil**, *Myriophyllum verticillatum*. Flooded pits

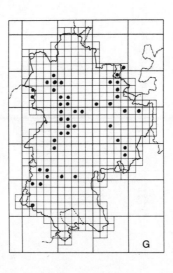

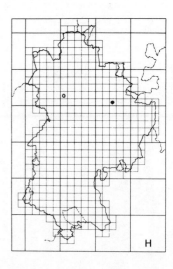

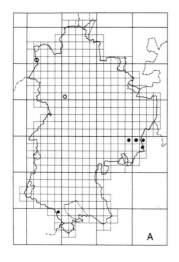

A

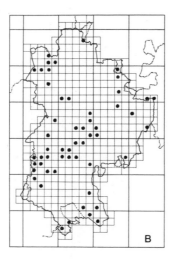

B

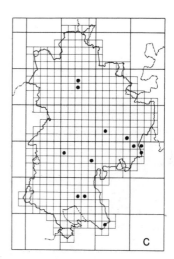

C

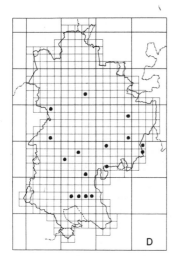

D

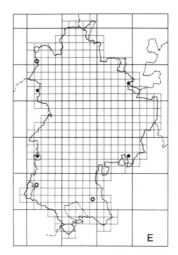

E

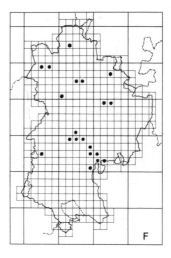

F

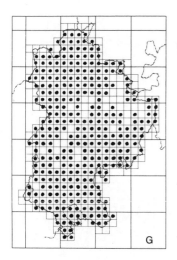

G

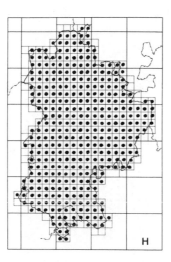

H

A **Mare's-tail**, *Hippuris vulgaris*. Lakes and rivers

B **Common Water-starwort***, *Callitriche stagnalis*. Wet places and woodland rides

C **Blunt-fruited Water-starwort***, *Callitriche obtusangula*. Ponds and rivers

D **Various-leaved Water-starwort***, *Callitriche platycarpa*. Ponds and rivers

E **Intermediate Water-starwort***, *Callitriche intermedia*. Flooded pits

F **Mistletoe**, *Viscum album*. Parasite on trees

G **Dogwood**, *Swida sanguinea* (*Thelycrania s.*). Hedgerows

H **Ivy**, *Hedera helix*. Woods and hedgerows

* All water-starworts are under-recorded as they can be identified only when they fruit which they do rarely.

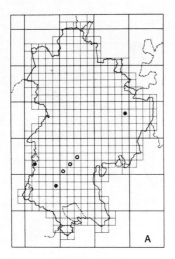

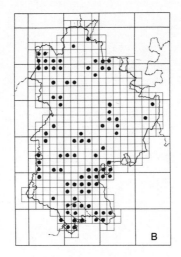

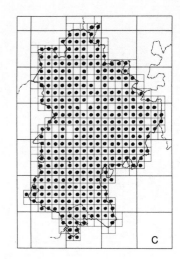

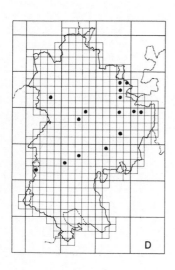

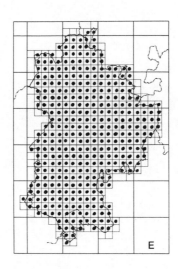

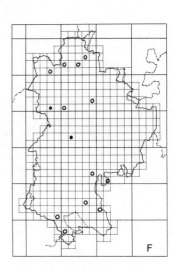

A **Marsh Pennywort**, *Hydrocotyle vulgaris*. Marshes

B **Sanicle**, *Sanicula europaea*. Woods

C **Rough Chervil**, *Chaerophyllum temulentum*. Hedgerows

D **Bur Chervil**, *Anthriscus caucalis*. Sandy banks

E **Cow Parsley**, *Anthriscus sylvestris*. Hedgerows

F **Shepherd's-needle**, *Scandix pecten-veneris*. Arable land

G **Upright Hedge-parsley**, *Torilis japonica*. Hedgerows

H **Spreading Hedge-parsley**, *Torilis arvensis*. Arable land

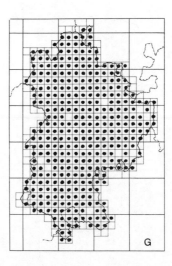

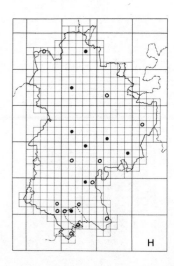

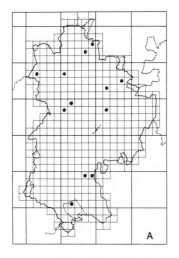

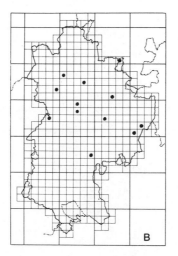

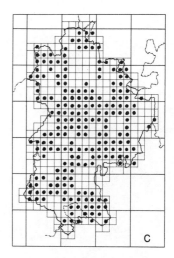

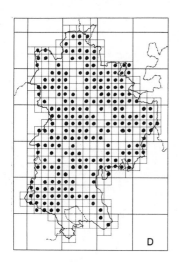

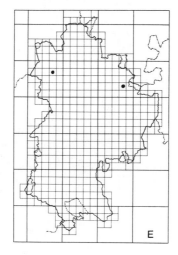

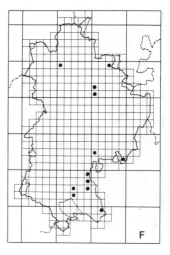

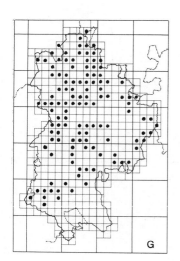

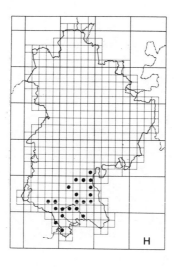

A **Knotted Hedge-parsley**, *Torilis nodosa*. Hedgebanks

B **Alexanders**, *Smyrnium olusatrum*. Roadsides

C **Hemlock**, *Conium maculatum*. Wet and waste places

D **Fool's Water-cress**, *Apium nodiflorum*. Ponds and riversides

E **Lesser Marshwort**, *Apium inundatum*. Sides of ponds

F **Corn Parsley**, *Petroselinum segetum*. Hedgebanks

G **Stone Parsley**, *Sison amomum*. Pastures and hedgerows

H **Great Pignut**, *Bunium bulbocastanum*. Disturbed chalky ground

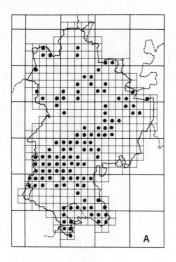

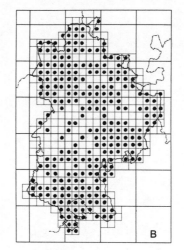

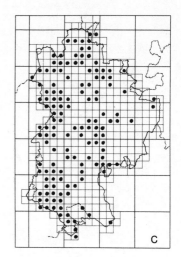

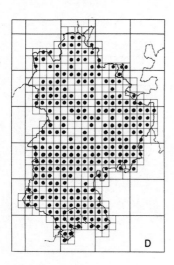

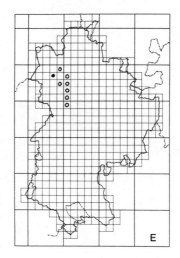

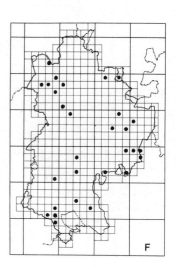

A **Pignut**, *Conopodium majus.* Woods and pastures

B **Burnet-saxifrage**, *Pimpinella saxifraga.* Pastures

C **Greater Burnet-saxifrage**, *Pimpinella major.* Woods and hedgerows

D **Ground-elder**, *Aegopodium podagraria.* Garden weed and waste places

E **Greater Water-parsnip**, *Sium latifolium.* Riversides and ditches

F **Lesser Water-parsnip**, *Berula erecta.* Streams

G **Moon Carrot**, *Seseli libanotis.* Chalk downland

H **Tubular Water-dropwort**, *Oenanthe fistulosa.* Wet places

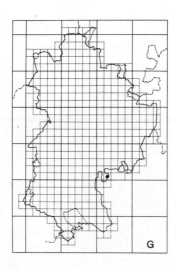

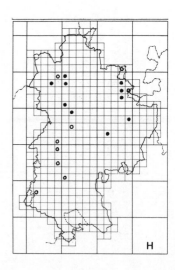

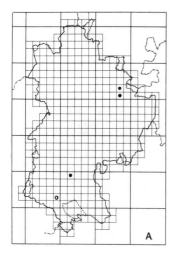

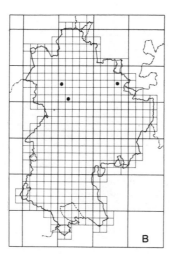

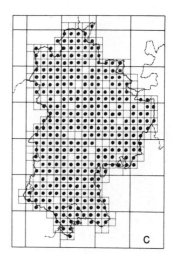

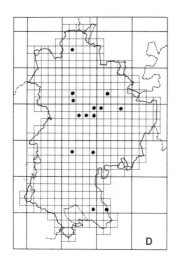

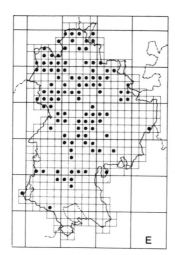

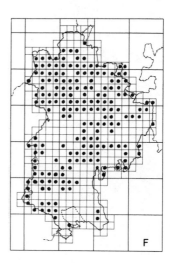

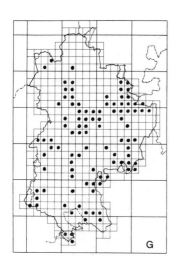

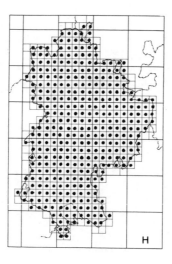

A **Parsley Water-dropwort**, *Oenanthe lachenalii*. Meadows and ditches

B **Fine-leaved Water-dropwort**, *Oenanthe aquatica*. Wet places

C **Fool's Parsley**, *Aethusa cynapium*. Arable land

D **Fennel**, *Foeniculum vulgare*. Waste places

E **Pepper-saxifrage**, *Silaum silaus*. Pastures

F **Wild Angelica**, *Angelica sylvestris*. Wet places

G **Wild Parsnip**, *Pastinaca sativa*. Calcareous pastures and waste places

H **Hogweed**, *Heracleum sphondylium*. Roadsides

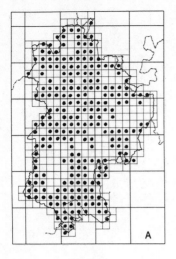

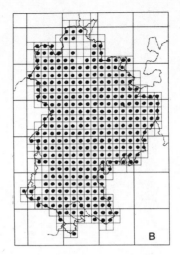

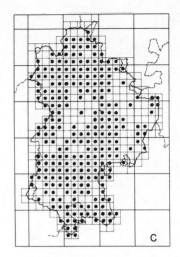

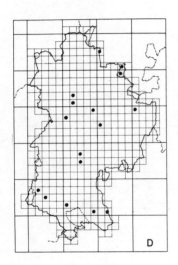

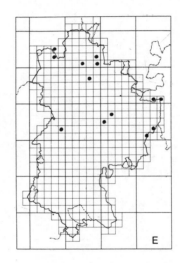

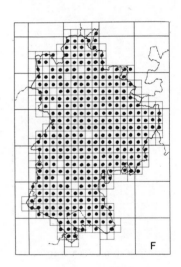

A **Wild Carrot**, *Daucus carota*.
Calcareous pastures

B **White Bryony**, *Bryonia dioica*.
Hedgerows

C **Dog's Mercury**, *Mercurialis perennis*. Woods

D **Annual Mercury**, *Mercurialis annua*.
Waste places

E **Broad-leaved Spurge**, *Euphorbia platyphyllos*. Arable land

F **Petty Spurge**, *Euphorbia peplus*.
Garden weed

G **Dwarf Spurge**, *Euphorbia exigua*.
Arable land

H **Wood Spurge**, *Euphorbia amygdaloides*. Woods

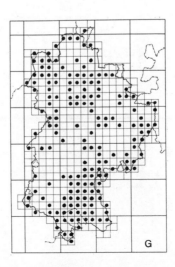

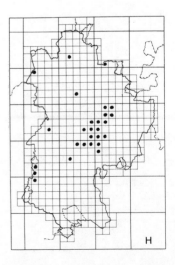

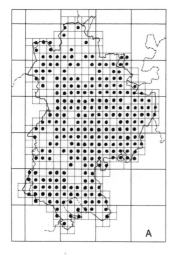

A

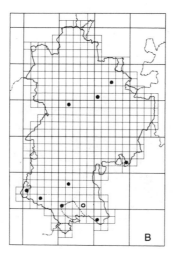

B

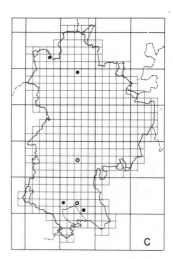

C

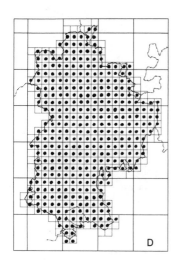

D

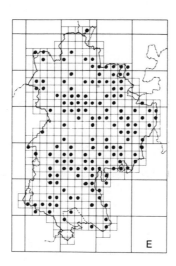

E

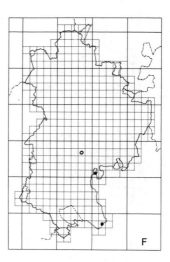

F

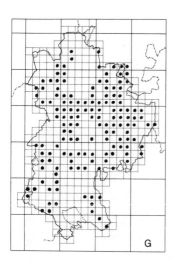

G

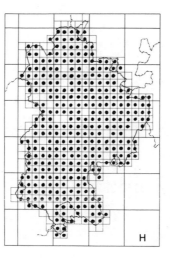

H

A **Sun Spurge**, *Euphorbia helioscopia*. Arable land

B **Twiggy Spurge**, *Euphorbia uralensis*, (including *E. esula*). Waste places

C **Cypress Spurge**, *Euphorbia cyparissias*. Waste places

D **Knotgrass**, *Polygonum aviculare*. Arable land and waste places

E *Polygonum aequale*. Farm trackways

F **Common Bistort**, *Polygonum bistorta*. Pastures

G **Amphibious Bistort**, *Polygonum amphibium*. Lakes and flooded pits

H **Redshank**, *Polygonum persicaria*. Arable land and waste places

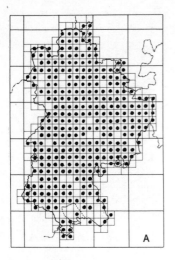

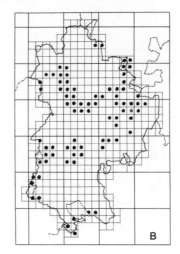

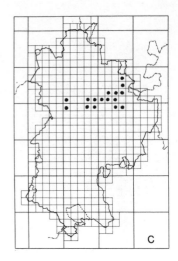

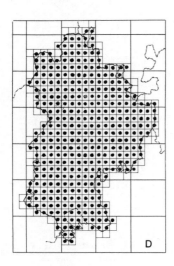

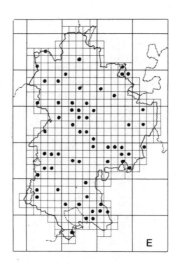

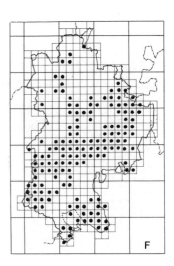

A **Pale Persicaria**, *Polygonum lapathi-folium* (including *P. nodosum*). Arable land

B **Water-pepper**, *Polygonum hydro-piper*. Riversides, and woodland rides

C **Tasteless Water-pepper**, *Polygonum mite*. Riversides

D **Black-bindweed**, *Polygonum convolvulus*. Arable land

E **Japanese Knotweed**, *Polygonum cuspidatum*. Waste places

F **Sheep's Sorrel**, *Rumex acetosella*. Heaths etc

G **Common Sorrel**, *Rumex acetosa*. Pastures

H **Water Dock**, *Rumex hydrolapathum*. Riversides

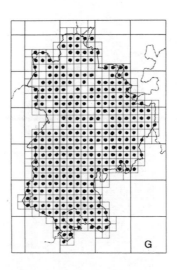

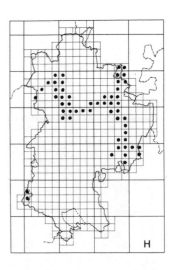

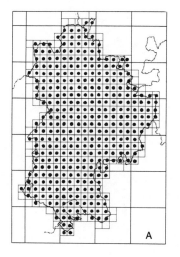

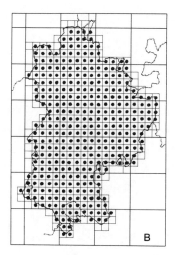

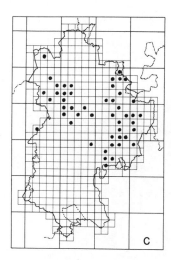

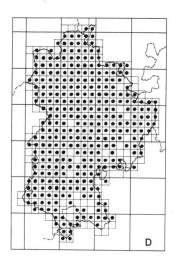

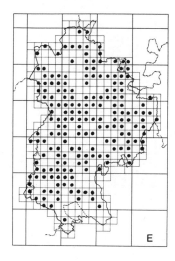

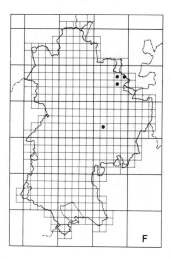

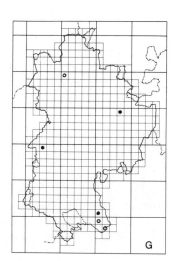

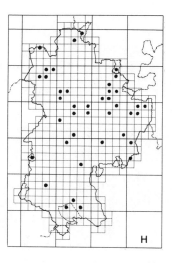

A **Curled Dock**, *Rumex crispus*. Waste places

B **Broad-leaved Dock**, *Rumex obtusifolius*. Waste places

C **Fiddle Dock**, *Rumex pulcher*. Pastures

D **Wood Dock**, *Rumex sanguineus*. Woods and shady places

E **Clustered Dock**, *Rumex conglomeratus*. Marshes

F **Marsh Dock**, *Rumex palustris*. Wet places

G **Golden Dock**, *Rumex maritimus*. Wet places

H **Pellitory-of-the-wall**, *Parietaria judaica* (*P. diffusa*). Old walls

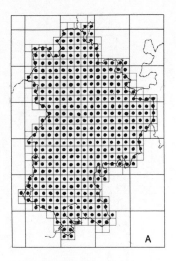

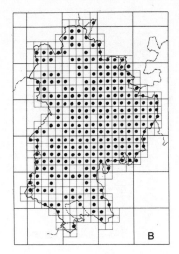

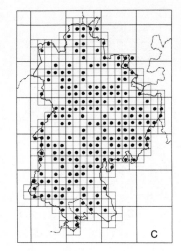

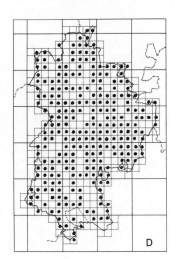

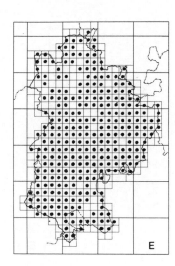

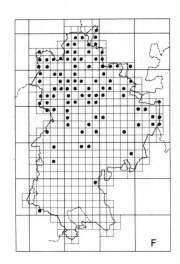

A **Common Nettle**, *Urtica dioica.* Ubiquitous

B **Small Nettle**, *Urtica urens.* Arable land

C **Hop**, *Humulus lupulus.* Hedgerows

D **Wych Elm**, *Ulmus glabra.* Woods and hedgerows

E **English Elm**, *Ulmus procera,* Hedgerows

F **Small-leaved Elm***, *Ulmus carpinifolia.* Hedgerows

G **Silver Birch**, *Betula pendula.* Woods

H **Downy Birch**, *Betula pubescens.* Woods on damp soils

* For an alternative treatment of the small-leaved elms see the Flora

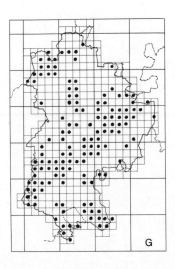

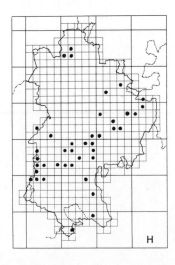

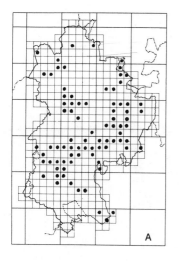

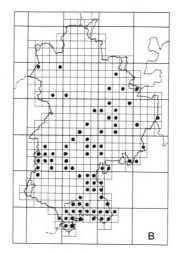

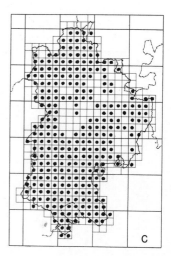

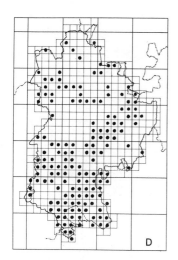

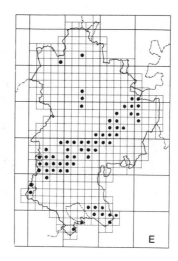

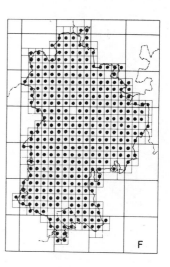

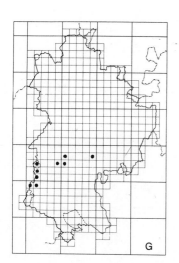

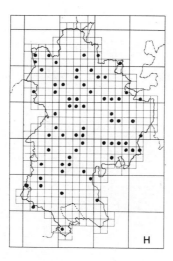

A **Alder**, *Alnus glutinosa*. Riversides

B **Hornbeam**, *Carpinus betulus*. Woods

C **Hazel**, *Corylus avellana*. Woods and hedgerows

D **Beech**, *Fagus sylvatica*. Woods

E **Sweet Chestnut**, *Castanea sativa*. A planted tree

F **Pedunculate Oak**, *Quercus robur*. Woods

G **Sessile Oak**, *Quercus petraea*. Woods

H **Grey Poplar**, *Populus canescens*. Roadsides

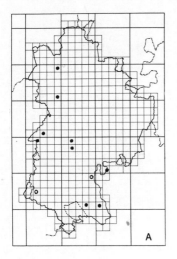

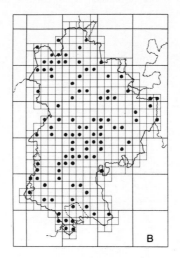

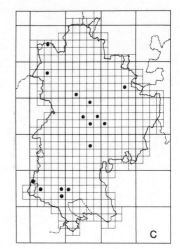

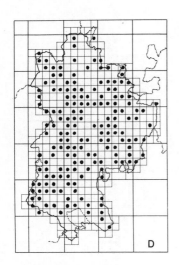

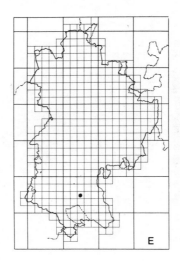

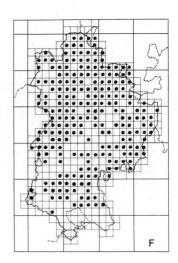

A **White Poplar**, *Populus alba*. Hedge-rows

B **Aspen**, *Populus tremula*. Woods

C **Black Poplar**, *Populus nigra*. River-sides

D **Italian Poplar**, *Populus canadensis*. Riversides and roadsides

E **Bay Willow**, *Salix pentandra*. River-sides

F **White Willow**, *Salix alba*. Riversides

G **Crack Willow**, *Salix fragilis*. River-sides

H **Almond Willow**, *Salix triandra*. Sides of ditches

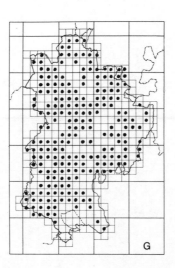

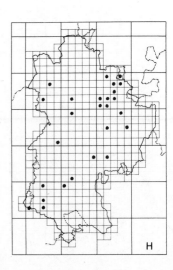

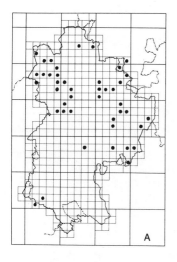

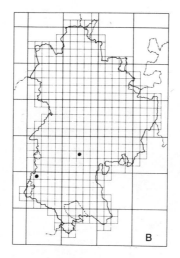

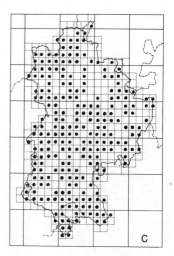

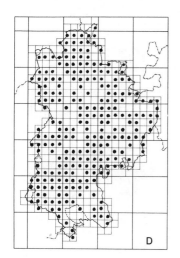

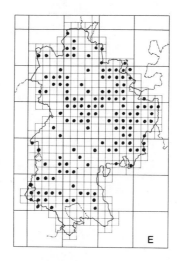

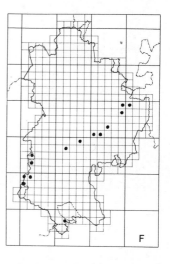

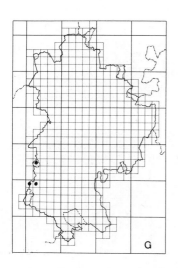

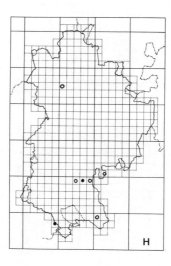

A **Purple Willow**, *Salix purpurea*. Riversides

B **Eared Willow**, *Salix aurita*. Woods and marshes

C **Goat Willow**, *Salix caprea*. Woods and hedgerows

D **Grey Willow**, *Salix cinerea, sensu lato*. Woods and wet places

E **Osier**, *Salix viminalis*. Riversides and sides of ditches

F **Heather**, *Calluna vulgaris*. Heaths

G **Bilberry**, *Vaccinium myrtillus*. Heaths

H **Yellow Bird's-nest**, *Monotropa hypopitys*. Woods

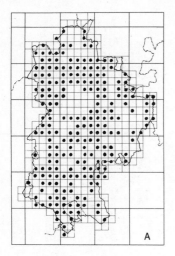

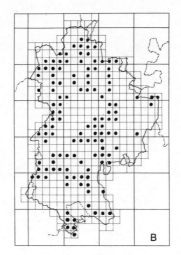

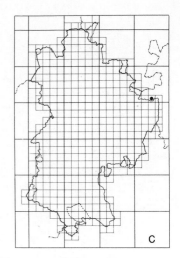

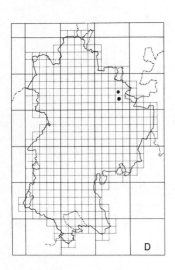

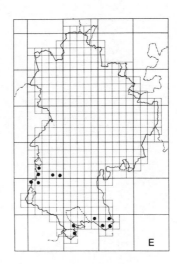

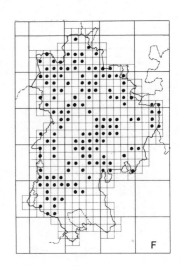

A **Cowslip**, *Primula veris.* Pastures

B **Primrose**, *Primula vulgaris.* Woods

C **Oxlip**, *Primula elatior.* Woods

D **Water-violet**, *Hottonia palustris.* Ponds

E **Yellow Pimpernel**, *Lysimachia nemorum.* Woods

F **Creeping-Jenny**, *Lysimachia nummularia.* Woods and hedgebanks

G **Yellow Loosestrife**, *Lysimachia vulgaris.* Riversides

H **Scarlet Pimpernel**, *Anagallis arvensis.* Arable land

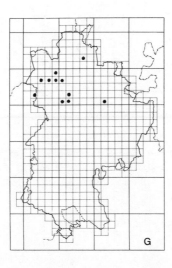

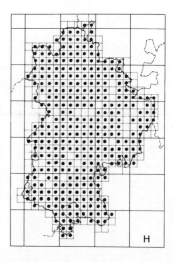

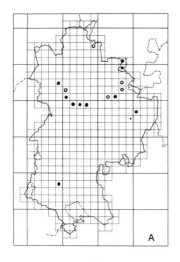

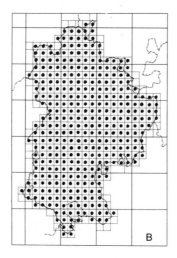

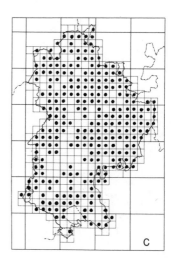

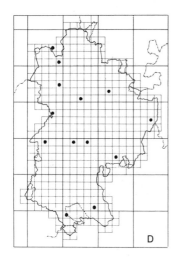

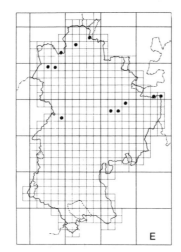

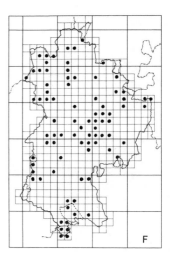

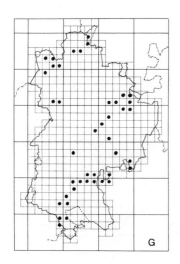

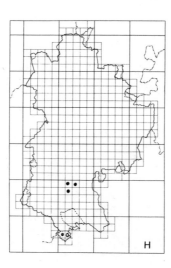

A **Brookweed**, *Samolus valerandi*. Riversides and marshes

B **Ash**, *Fraxinus excelsior*. Woods and hedgerows

C **Privet**, *Ligustrum vulgare*. Hedgerows and scrub

D **Lesser Periwinkle**, *Vinca minor*. Naturalised in woods, etc

E **Lesser Centaury**, *Centaurium pulchellum*. Woodland rides

F **Common Centaury**, *Centaurium erythraea* (*C. minus*). Pastures

G **Yellow-wort**, *Blackstonia perfoliata*. Calcareous pastures

H **Chiltern Gentian**, *Gentianella germanica*. Chalk downland

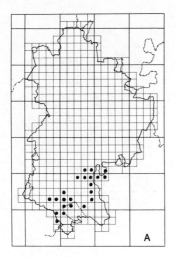

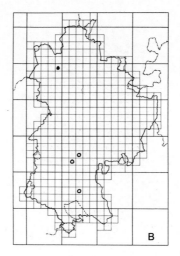

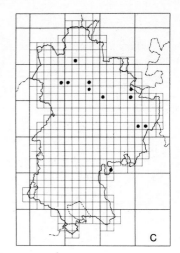

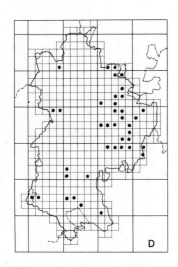

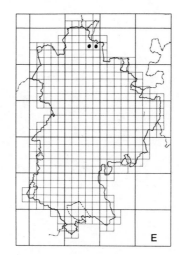

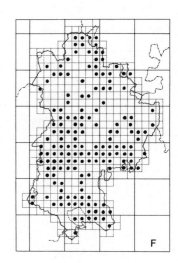

A **Autumn Gentian**, *Gentianella amarella*. Chalk downland

B **Bogbean**, *Menyanthes trifoliata*. Wet places

C **Hound's-tongue**, *Cynoglossum officinale*. Woods and rough pastures

D **Common Comfrey**, *Symphytum officinale*. Riversides

E **White Comfrey**, *Symphytum orientale*. Roadsides

F **Russian Comfrey**, *Symphytum × uplandicum (S. peregrinum)*. Roadsides and waste places

G **Tuberous Comfrey**, *Symphytum tuberosum*. Derelict gardens

H **Bugloss**, *Lycopsis arvensis*. Sandy fields

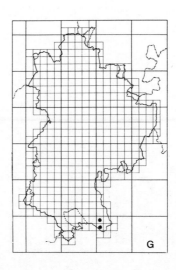

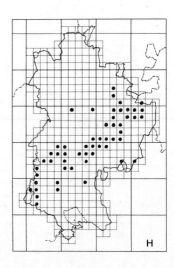

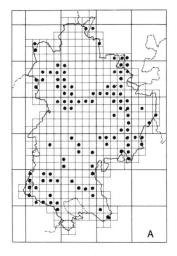

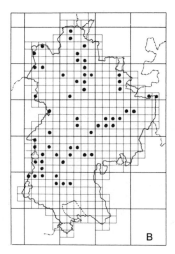

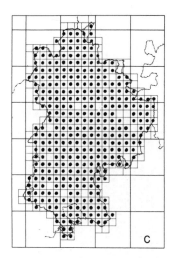

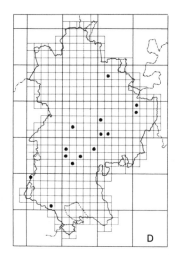

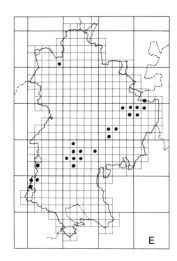

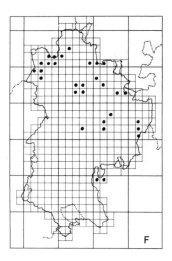

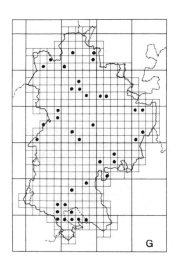

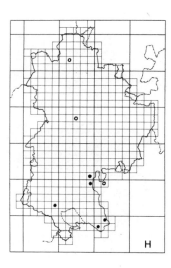

A **Water Forget-me-not**, *Myosotis scorpioides*. Wet places

B **Tufted Forget-me-not**, *Myosotis caespitosa*. Sides of ponds

C **Field Forget-me-not**, *Myosotis arvensis*. Arable land and waste places

D **Changing Forget-me-not**, *Myosotis discolor*. Heathy places and railway banks

E **Early Forget-me-not**, *Myosotis ramosissima* (*M. hispida*). Heathy places and railway banks

F **Common Gromwell**, *Lithospermum officinale*. Field borders

G **Field Gromwell**, *Lithospermum arvense*. Arable land

H **Viper's-bugloss**, *Echium vulgare*. Rough pastures

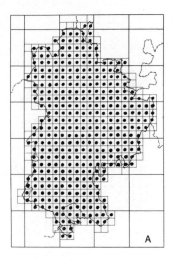

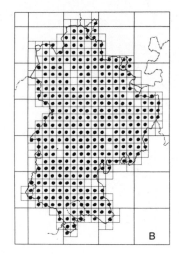

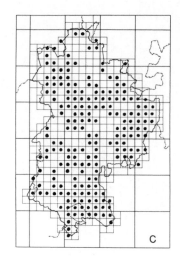

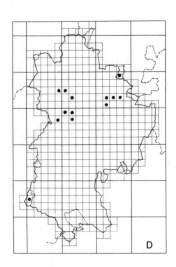

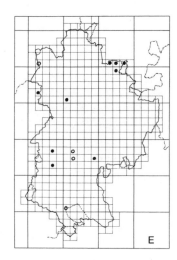

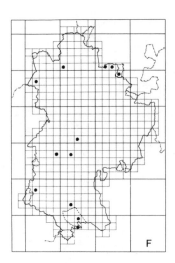

A **Field Bindweed**, *Convolvulus arvensis*. Arable land and roadsides

B **Hedge Bindweed**, *Calystegia sepium*. Hedgerows

C **Large Bindweed**, *Calystegia sylvatica* (*C. sylvestris*). Hedgerows

D **Greater Dodder**, *Cuscuta europaea*. Riversides

E **Deadly Nightshade**, *Atropa bella-donna*. Rough pastures

F **Henbane**, *Hyoscyamus niger*. Waste places

G **Bittersweet**, *Solanum dulcamara*. Hedgerows

H **Black Nightshade**, *Solanum nigrum*. Arable land

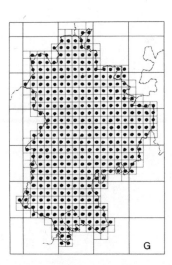

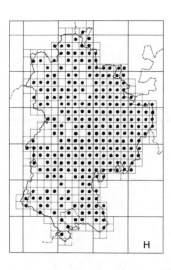

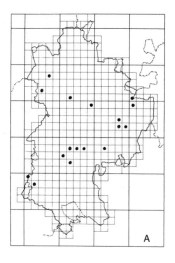

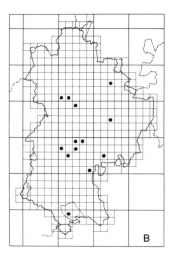

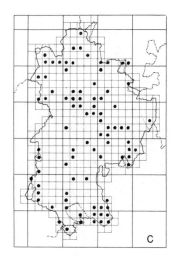

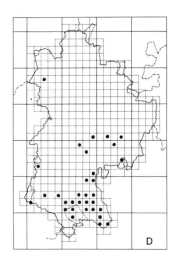

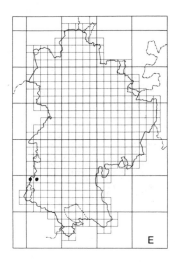

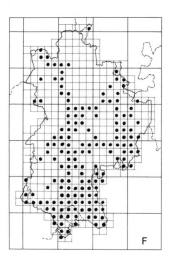

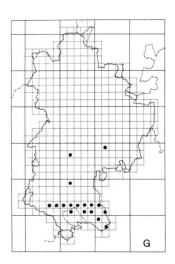

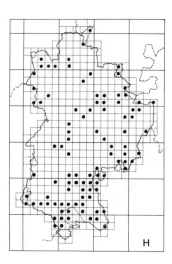

A **Green Nightshade**, *Solanum sarrachoides*. Arable land

B **Thorn-apple**, *Datura stramonium*. Waste places and arable land

C **Great Mullein**, *Verbascum thapsus*. Waste places and rough pastures

D **Dark Mullein**, *Verbascum nigrum*. Rough pastures

E **Lesser Snapdragon**, *Misopates orontium* (*Antirrhinum o.*). Arable land

F **Common Toadflax**, *Linaria vulgaris*. Waste places and roadsides

G **Pale Toadflax**, *Linaria repens*. Chalky fields and railway ballast

H **Small Toadflax**, *Chaenorhinum minus*. Arable land and railway ballast

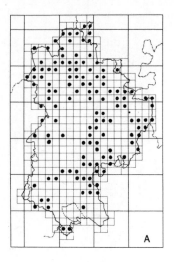

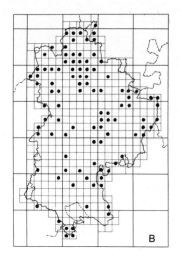

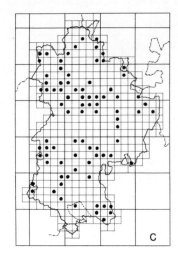

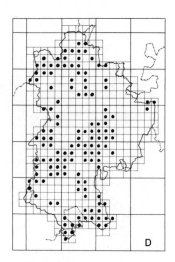

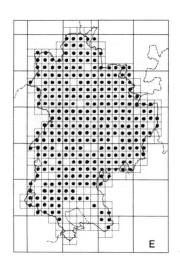

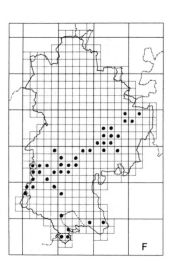

A **Round-leaved Fluellen**, *Kickxia spuria*. Arable land

B **Sharp-leaved Fluellen**, *Kickxia elatine*. Arable land

C **Ivy-leaved Toadflax**, *Cymbalaria muralis*. Walls

D **Common Figwort**, *Scrophularia nodosa*. Woods

E **Water Figwort**, *Scrophularia auriculata* (*S. aquatica*). Wet places

F **Foxglove**, *Digitalis purpurea*. Woods

G **Brooklime**, *Veronica beccabunga*. Wet places

H **Marsh Speedwell**, *Veronica scutellata*. Sides of ponds

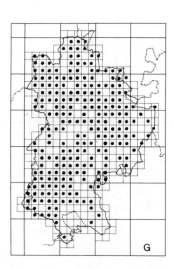

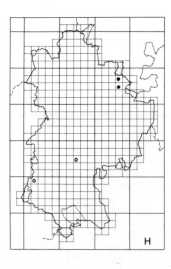

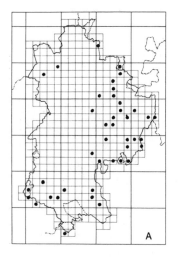

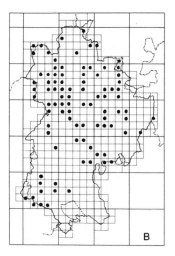

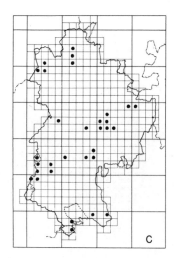

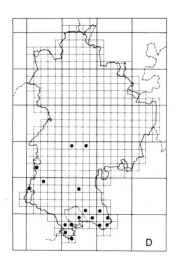

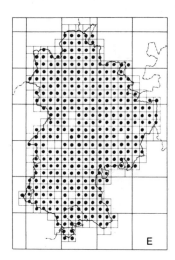

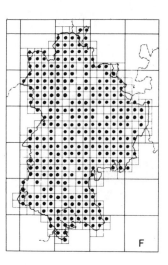

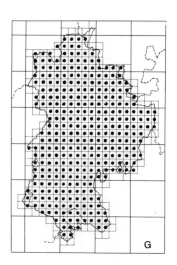

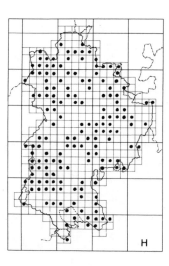

A **Blue Water-speedwell**, *Veronica anagallis-aquatica*. Streams

B **Pink Water-speedwell**, *Veronica catenata*. Sides of ponds

C **Heath Speedwell**, *Veronica officinalis*. Heaths

D **Wood Speedwell**, *Veronica montana*. Woods

E **Germander Speedwell**, *Veronica chamaedrys*. Hedgebanks and pastures

F **Wall Speedwell**, *Veronica arvensis*. Arable land and bare places

G **Ivy-leaved Speedwell**, *Veronica hederifolia*. Hedgebanks and arable land

H **Thyme-leaved Speedwell**, *Veronica serpyllifolia*. Pastures and woodland rides

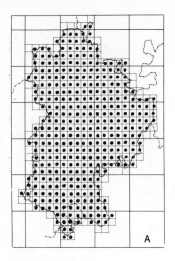

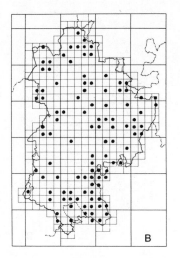

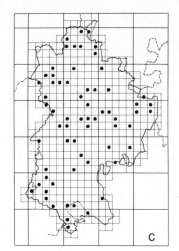

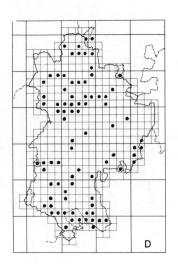

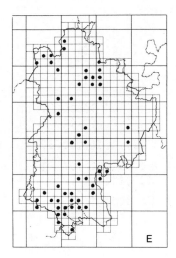

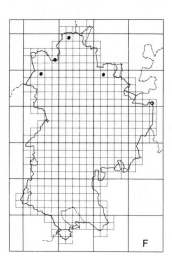

A **Common Field-speedwell**, *Veronica persica*. Arable land

B **Grey Field-speedwell**, *Veronica polita*. Arable land

C **Green Field-speedwell**, *Veronica agrestis*. Arable land

D **Slender Speedwell**, *Veronica filiformis*. Lawns

E **Yellow Rattle**, *Rhinanthus minor* (*R. crista-galli*). Pastures

F **Crested Cow-wheat**, *Melampyrum cristatum*. Pastures

G **Field Cow-wheat**, *Melampyrum arvense*. Hedgebanks

H **Eyebright**, *Euphrasia nemorosa*. Calcareous pastures and woodland rides

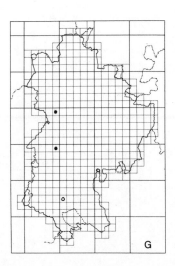

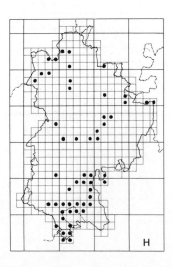

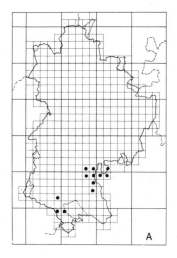

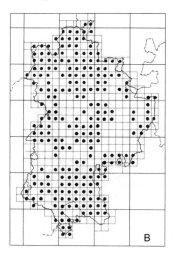

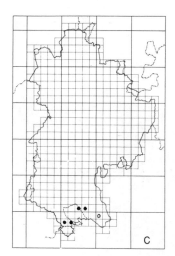

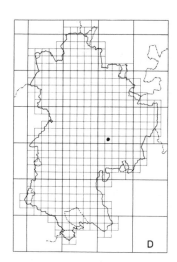

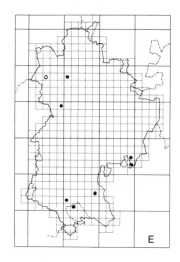

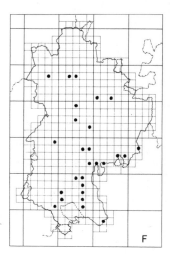

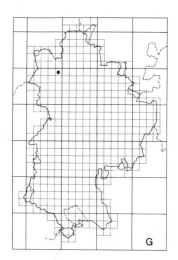

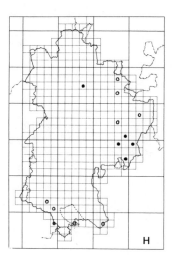

A *Euphrasia pseudo-kerneri.* Chalk downland

B **Red Bartsia**, *Odontites verna.* Pastures

C **Toothwort**, *Lathraea squamaria.*
   Woods, parasite on Hazel

D **Greater Broomrape**, *Orobanche
   rapum-genistae.* Heaths, parasite on
   Broom

E **Knapweed Broomrape**, *Orobanche
   elatior.* Rough pastures, parasite on
   Greater Knapweed

F **Common Broomrape**, *Orobanche
   minor.* Pastures, parasite on various
   other species

G **Bladderwort**, *Utricularia australis.*
   Flooded pits

H **Vervain**, *Verbena officinalis.* Rough
   pastures

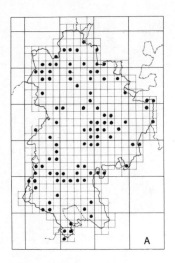

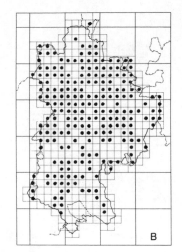

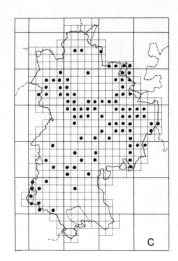

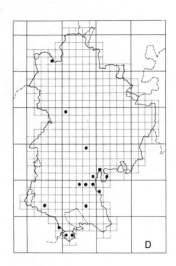

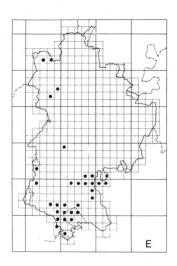

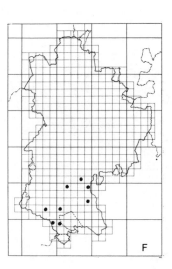

A **Corn Mint**, *Mentha arvensis*. Woodland rides and arable fields

B **Water Mint**, *Mentha aquatica*. Wet places

C **Gipsywort**, *Lycopus europaeus*. Wet places

D **Marjoram**, *Origanum vulgare*. Calcareous pastures

E **Large Thyme**, *Thymus pulegioides*. Calcareous pastures

F **Common Thyme**, *Thymus drucei*. Chalk downland

G **Common Calamint**, *Calamintha ascendens*. Hedgebanks

H **Basil Thyme**, *Acinos arvensis*. Calcareous pastures and railway banks

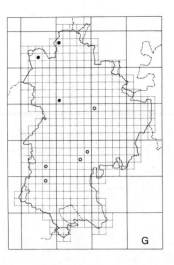

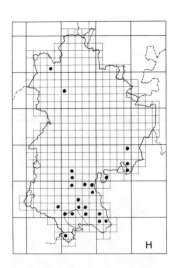

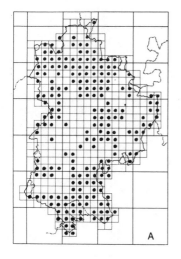

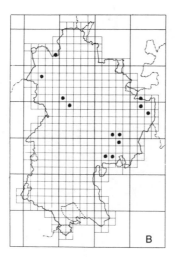

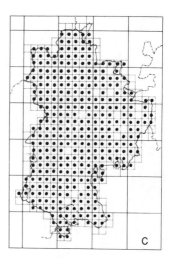

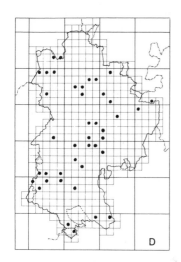

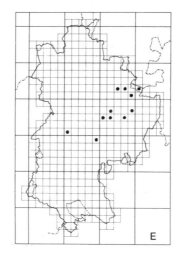

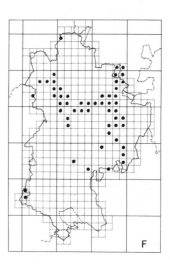

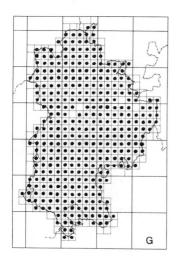

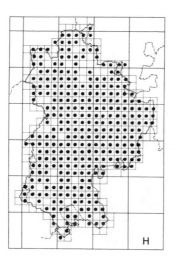

A **Wild Basil**, *Clinopodium vulgare*.
Hedgebanks

B **Wild Clary**, *Salvia horminoides*.
Pastures

C **Selfheal**, *Prunella vulgaris*. Pastures

D **Betony**, *Betonica officinalis* (*Stachys
o.*). Pastures and woodland rides

E **Field Woundwort**, *Stachys arvensis*.
Arable land

F **Marsh Woundwort**, *Stachys
palustris*. Riversides

G **Hedge Woundwort**, *Stachys
sylvatica*. Hedgebanks

H **Black Horehound**, *Ballota nigra*.
Hedgebanks

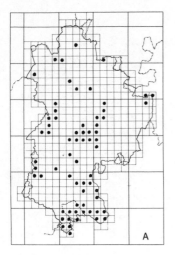

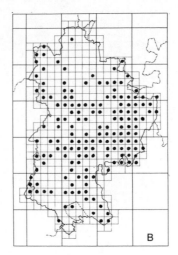

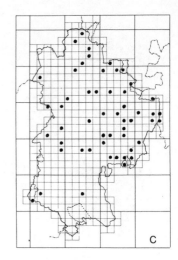

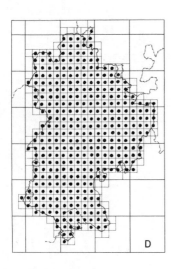

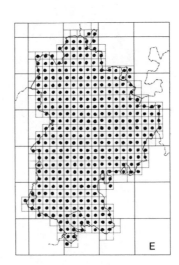

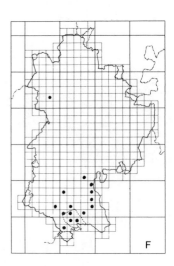

A **Yellow Archangel**, *Lamiastrum galeobdolon* (*Galeobdolon luteum*). Woods

B **Henbit Dead-nettle**, *Lamium amplexicaule*. Arable land

C **Cut-leaved Dead-nettle**, *Lamium hybridum*. Arable land

D **Red Dead-nettle**, *Lamium purpureum*. Arable land

E **White Dead-nettle**, *Lamium album*. Hedgerows

F **Red Hemp-nettle**, *Galeopsis angustifolia*. Arable land

G **Common Hemp-nettle**, *Galeopsis tetrahit* (including *G. bifida*). Hedge-banks and woodland borders

H **Cat-mint**, *Nepeta cataria*. Hedge-banks

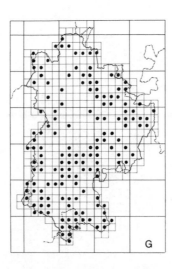

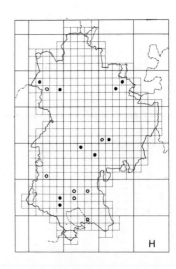

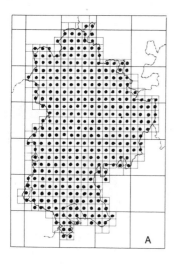

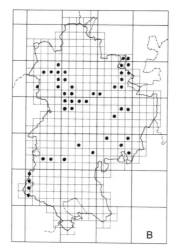

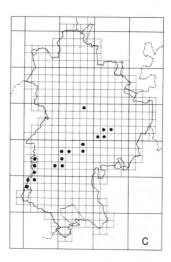

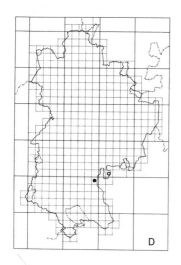

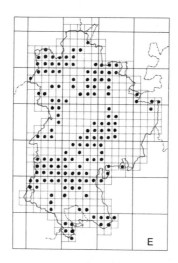

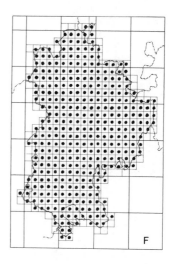

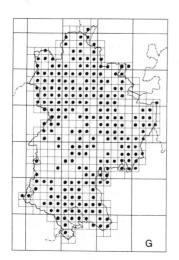

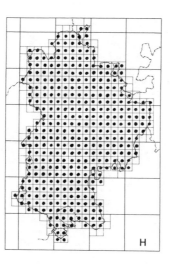

A **Ground-ivy**, *Glechoma nederacea.* Hedgebanks and woodland rides

B **Skullcap**, *Scutellaria galericulata.* Riversides

C **Wood Sage**, *Teucrium scorodonia.* Woodland borders

D **Ground-pine**, *Ajuga chamaepitys.* Chalky fields

E **Bugle**, *Ajuga reptans.* Woods and pastures

F **Greater Plantain**, *Plantago major.* Ubiquitous

G **Hoary Plantain**, *Plantago media.* Pastures

H **Ribwort Plantain**, *Plantago lanceolata.* Ubiquitous

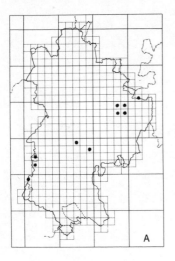

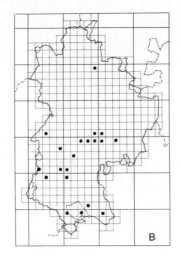

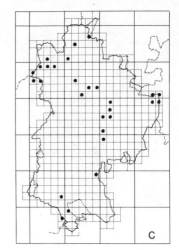

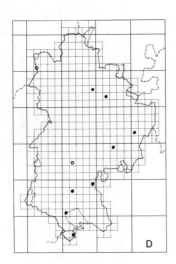

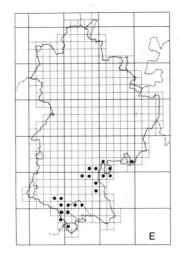

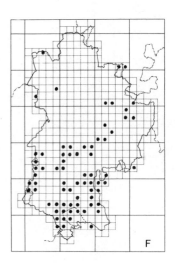

A **Buck's-horn Plantain**, *Plantago coronopus*. Bare sandy ground

B **Giant Bellflower**, *Campanula latifolia*. Woods

C **Nettle-leaved Bellflower**, *Campanula trachelium*. Woods

D **Creeping Bellflower**, *Campanula rapunculoides*. Rough pastures

E **Clustered Bellflower**, *Campanula glomerata*. Chalk downland

F **Harebell**, *Campanula rotundifolia*. Pastures

G **Venus's-looking-glass**, *Legousia hybrida*. Arable land

H **Sheep's-bit**, *Jasione montana*. Sandy pastures

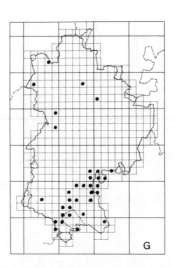

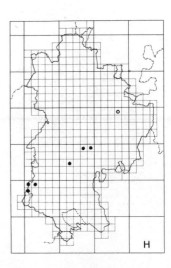

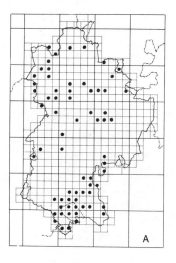

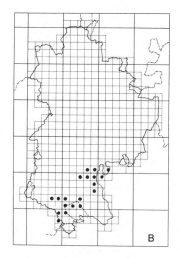

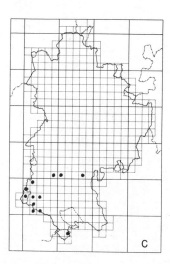

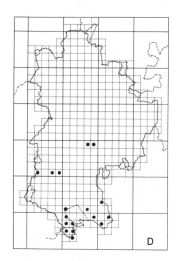

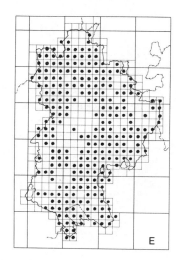

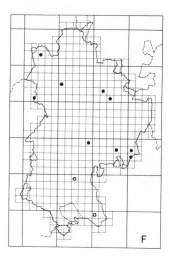

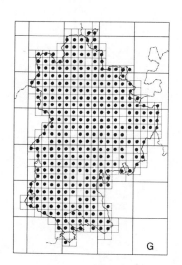

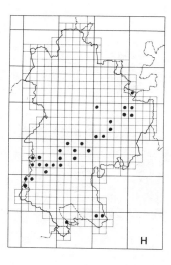

A **Field Madder**, *Sherardia arvensis*. Arable land

B **Squinancywort**, *Asperula cynanchica*. Chalk downland

C **Crosswort**, *Cruciata laevipes* (*Galium cruciata*). Rough pastures

D **Woodruff**, *Galium odoratum* (*Asperula odorata*). Woods

E **Hedge Bedstraw**, *Galium mollugo* subsp. *mollugo*. Hedgerows and rough pastures

F *Galium mollugo* subsp. *erectum* (*G. erectum*). Hedgerows and rough pastures

G **Lady's Bedstraw**, *Galium verum*. Pastures

H **Heath Bedstraw**, *Galium saxatile*. Heaths

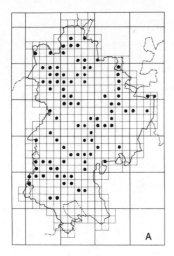

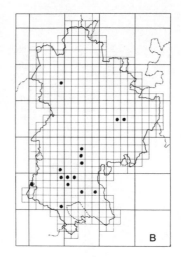

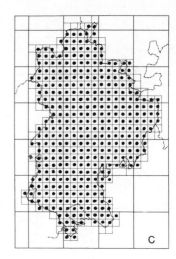

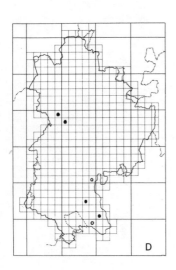

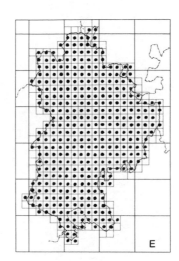

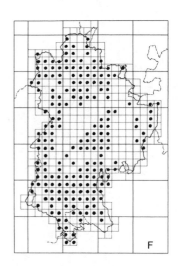

A **Common Marsh-bedstraw**, *Galium palustre*. Wet places

B **Fen Bedstraw**, *Galium uliginosum*. Marshes

C **Cleavers**, *Galium aparine*. Hedgerows and arable land

D **Dwarf Elder**, *Sambucus ebulus*. Roadsides

E **Elder**, *Sambucus nigra*. Woods and hedgerows

F **Wayfaring-tree**, *Viburnum lantana*. Hedgerows

G **Guelder-rose**, *Viburnum opulus*. Woods and hedgerows

H **Honeysuckle**, *Lonicera periclymenum*. Woods and hedgerows

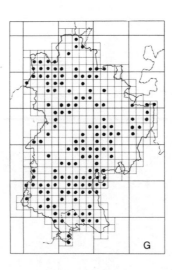

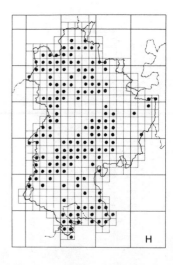

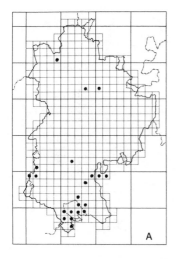

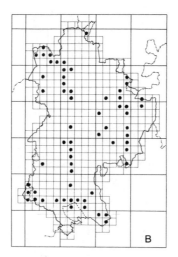

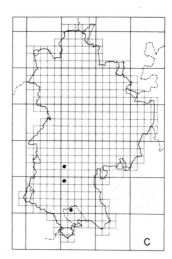

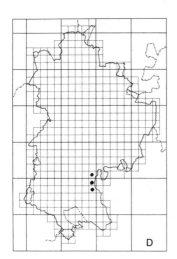

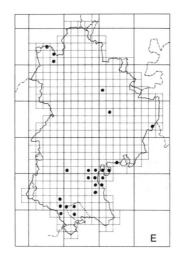

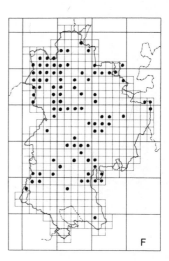

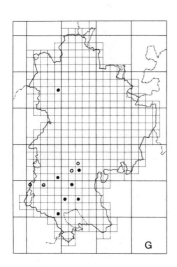

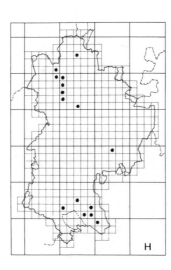

A **Moschatel**, *Adoxa moschatellina*. Woods

B **Common Cornsalad**, *Valerianella locusta*. Dry banks

C **Keel-fruited Cornsalad**, *Valerianella carinata*. Gardens

D **Broad-fruited Cornsalad**, *Valerianella rimosa*. Arable land

E **Narrow-fruited Cornsalad**, *Valerianella dentata*. Arable land

F **Common Valerian**, *Valeriana officinalis*. Woods and rough pastures

G **Marsh Valerian**, *Valeriana dioica*. Marshes

H **Red Valerian**, *Centranthus ruber*. Waste places and railway banks

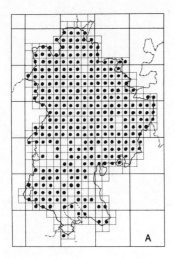

A

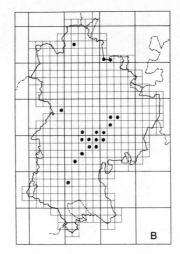

B

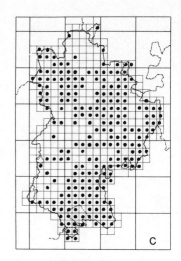

C

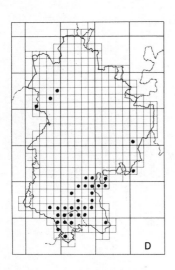

D

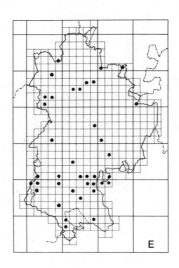

E

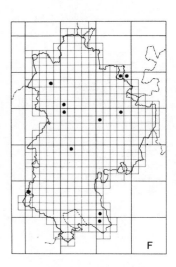

F

A **Teasel**, *Dipsacus fullonum*. Ditches and waste places

B **Small Teasel**, *Dipsacus pilosus.* Woods and streamsides

C **Field Scabious**, *Knautia arvensis.* Rough pastures and waste places

D **Small Scabious**, *Scabiosa columbaria*. Calcareous pastures

E **Devil's-bit Scabious**, *Succisa pratensis*. Woods and marshes

F **Nodding Bur-marigold**, *Bidens cernua*. Sides of ponds

G **Trifid Bur-marigold**, *Bidens tripartita*. Sides of rivers and ponds

H **Gallant Soldier**, *Galinsoga parviflora*. Sandy fields and waste places

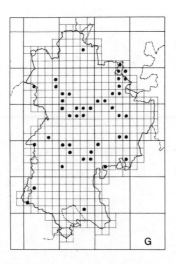

G

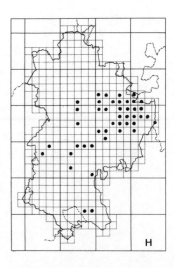

H

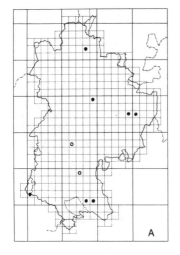

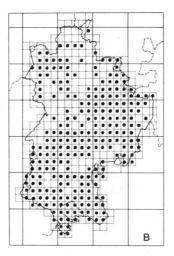

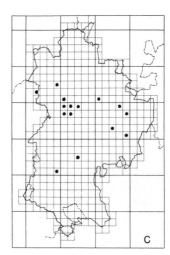

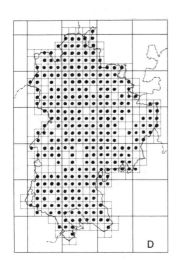

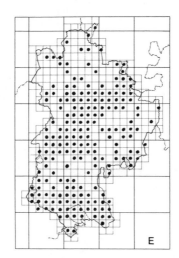

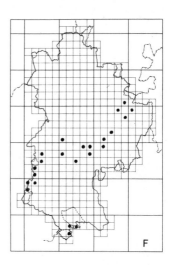

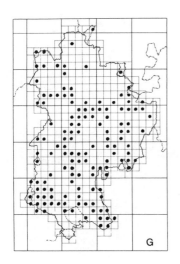

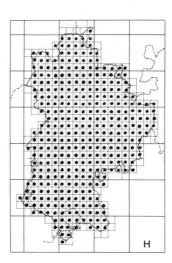

A **Shaggy Soldier**, *Galinsoga ciliata.*
Waste places

B **Common Ragwort**, *Senecio
jacobaea.* Pastures

C **Marsh Ragwort**, *Senecio aquaticus.*
Water meadows

D **Hoary Ragwort**, *Senecio erucifolius.*
Pastures and waste places

E **Oxford Ragwort**, *Senecio squalidus.*
Waste places

F **Wood Ragwort**, *Senecio sylvaticus.*
Cleared woodland on light soils

G **Sticky Groundsel**, *Senecio viscosus.*
Waste places

H **Groundsel**, *Senecio vulgaris.* Arable
land and waste places

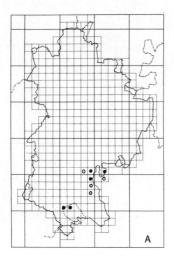

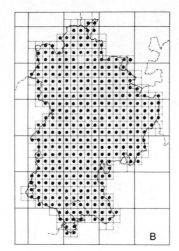

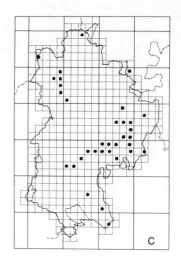

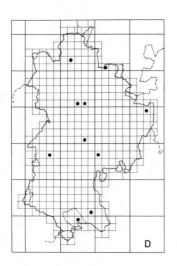

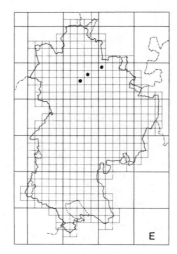

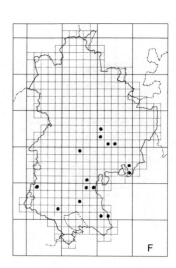

A **Field Fleawort**, *Senecio integrifolius*. Chalk downland

B **Colt's-foot**, *Tussilago farfara*. Waste places

C **Butterbur**, *Petasites hybridus*. Wet places

D **White Butterbur**, *Petasites fragrans*. Naturalised on roadsides

E **Elecampane**, *Inula helenium*. Hedgerows

F **Ploughman's-spikenard**, *Inula conyza*. Rough grassland

G **Common Fleabane**, *Pulicaria dysenterica*. Waterlogged pastures

H **Common Cudweed**, *Filago vulgaris* (*F. germanica*). Bare sandy ground

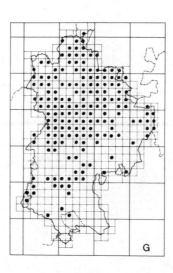

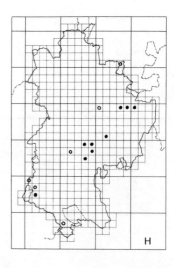

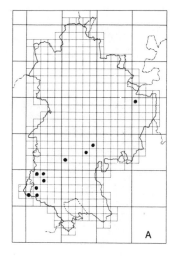

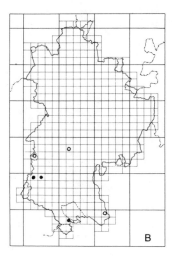

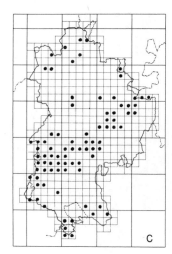

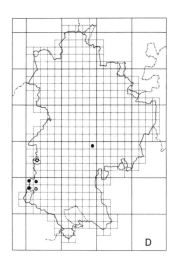

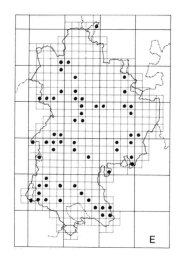

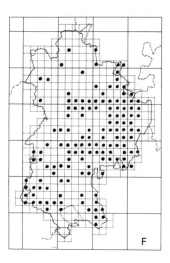

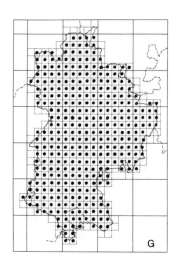

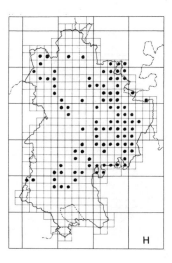

A **Small Cudweed**, *Filago minima*. Bare sandy ground

B **Wood Cudweed**, *Gnaphalium sylvaticum*. Woodland rides

C **Marsh Cudweed**, *Gnaphalium uliginosum*. Arable land and damp places

D **Goldenrod**, *Solidago virgaurea*. Heaths

E **Blue Fleabane**, *Erigeron acer*. Sides of brick pits and railway banks

F **Canadian Fleabane**, *Conyza canadensis (Erigeron c.)*. Waste places

G **Daisy**, *Bellis perennis*. Pastures

H **Hemp-agrimony**, *Eupatorium cannabinum*. Riversides and ditches

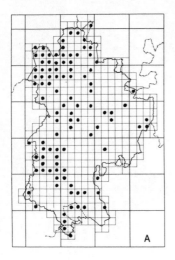

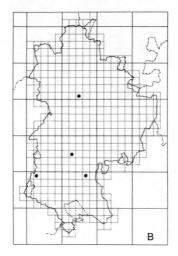

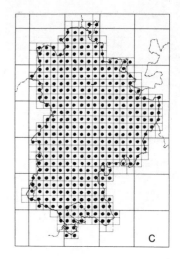

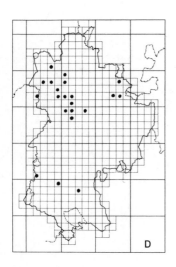

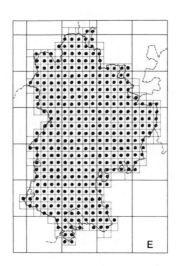

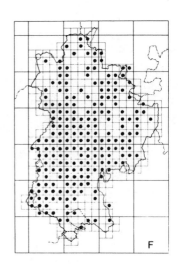

A **Stinking Chamomile**, *Anthemis cotula*. Arable land

B **Corn Chamomile**, *Anthemis arvensis*. Arable land

C **Yarrow**, *Achillea millefolium*. Pastures

D **Sneezewort**, *Achillea ptarmica*. Water meadows

E **Scentless Mayweed**, *Tripleurospermum maritima (Matricaria m.)*. Waste places

F **Scented Mayweed**, *Matricaria recutita*. Arable land

G **Pineappleweed**, *Matricaria matricarioides*. Waste places

H **Corn Marigold**, *Chrysanthemum segetum*. Arable land

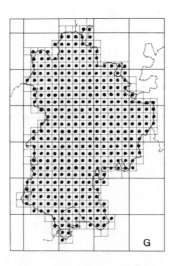

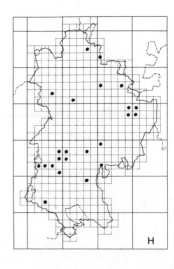

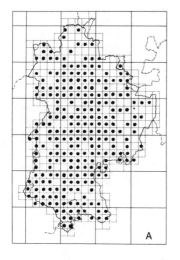

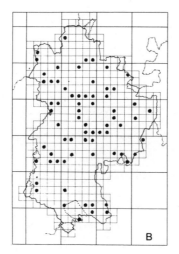

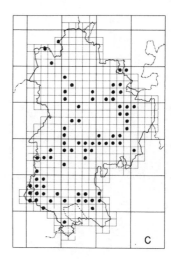

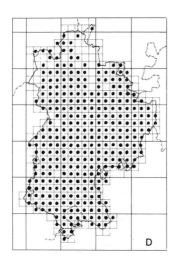

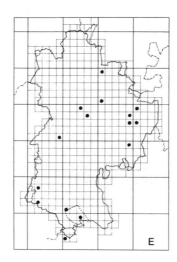

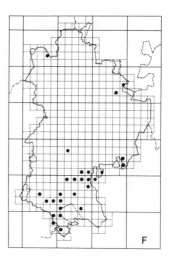

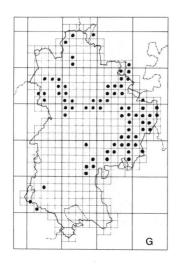

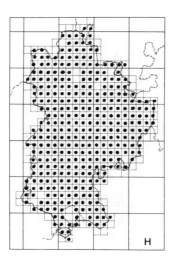

A **Ox-eye Daisy**, *Leucanthemum vulgare* (*Chrysanthemum leucanthemum*). Pastures

B **Feverfew**, *Tanacetum parthenium* (*Chrysanthemum p.*). Waste places

C **Tansy**, *Tanacetum vulgare*. Waste places

D **Mugwort**, *Artemisia vulgaris*. Waste places

E **Wormwood**, *Artemisia absinthium*. Waste places

F **Carline Thistle**, *Carlina vulgaris*. Calcareous pastures

G **Greater Burdock**, *Arctium lappa*. Wet places

H **Lesser Burdock**, *Arctium minus*, (including *A. nemorosum* and *A. vulgare*). Waste places and wood borders

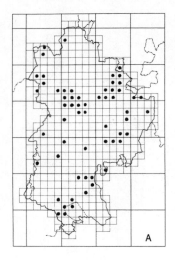

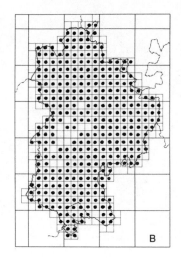

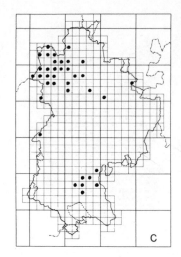

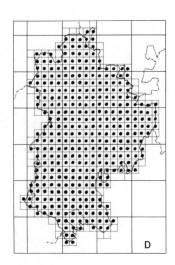

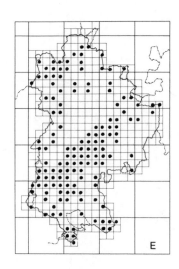

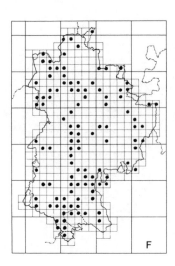

A **Musk Thistle**, *Carduus nutans*. Rough grassland

B **Welted Thistle**, *Carduus acanthoides* (*C. crispus*). Hedgerows

C **Woolly Thistle**, *Cirsium eriophorum*. Rough pastures

D **Spear Thistle**, *Cirsium vulgare*. Waste places

E **Marsh Thistle**, *Cirsium palustre*. Woods and marshes

F **Dwarf Thistle**, *Cirsium acaule*. Pastures

G **Creeping Thistle**, *Cirsium arvense*. Arable land and waste places

H **Greater Knapweed**, *Centaurea scabiosa*. Pastures

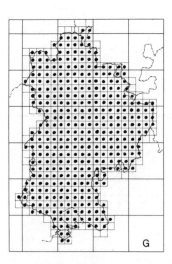

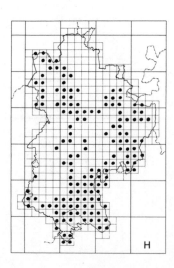

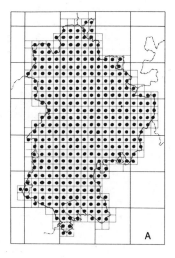

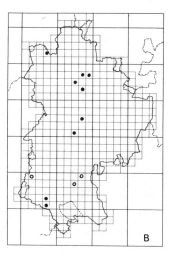

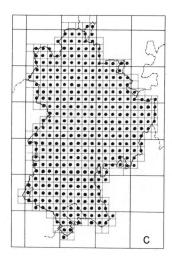

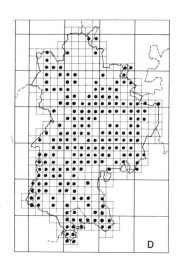

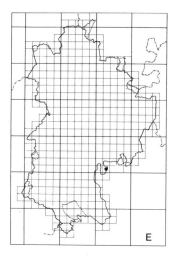

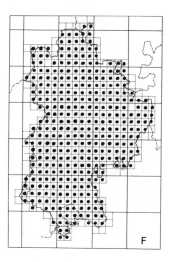

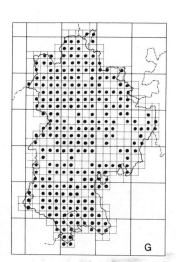

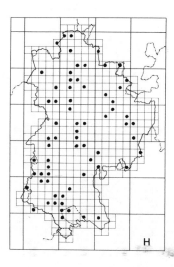

A **Common Knapweed**, *Centaurea nigra* (including *C. nemorosa*). Pastures

B **Saw-wort**, *Serratula tinctoria*. Pastures

C **Nipplewort**, *Lapsana communis*. Hedgerows and waste places

D **Cat's-ear**, *Hypochoeris radicata*. Pastures

E **Spotted Cat's-ear**, *Hypochoeris maculata*. Chalk downland

F **Autumn Hawkbit**, *Leontodon autumnalis*. Pastures and roadside verges

G **Rough Hawkbit**, *Leontodon hispidus*. Pastures

H **Lesser Hawkbit**, *Leontodon taraxacoides*. Pastures

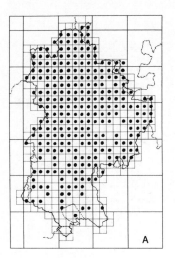

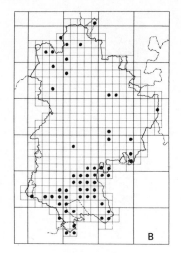

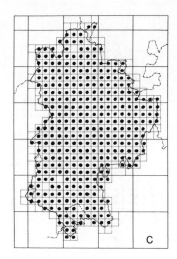

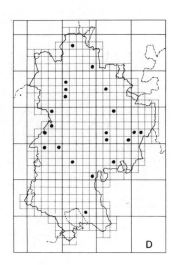

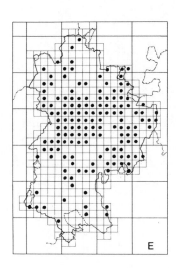

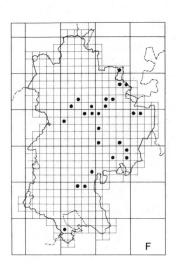

A **Bristly Oxtongue**, *Picris echioides*. Sides of ditches and rough pastures

B **Hawkweed Oxtongue**, *Picris hieracioides*. Calcareous pastures

C **Goat's-beard**, *Tragopogon pratensis* subsp. *minor*. Pastures

D *Tragopogon pratensis* subsp. *pratensis*. Roadside verges

E **Prickly Lettuce**, *Lactuca serriola*. Waste places

F **Great Lettuce**, *Lactuca virosa*. Waste places

G **Wall Lettuce**, *Mycelis muralis*. Wood borders and walls

H **Perennial Sow-thistle**, *Sonchus arvensis*. Arable land and waste places

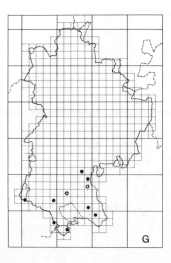

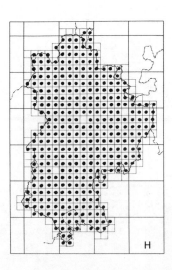

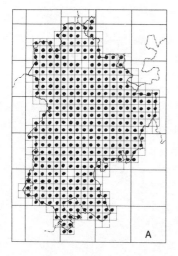

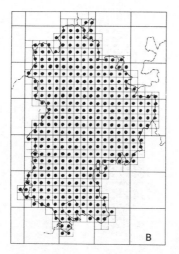

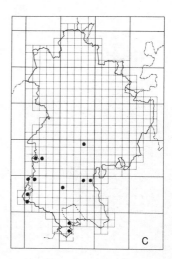

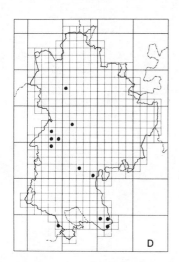

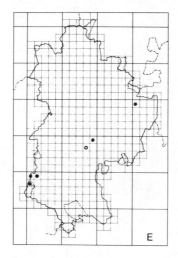

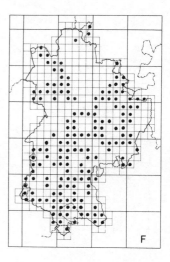

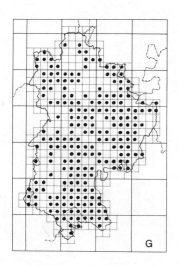

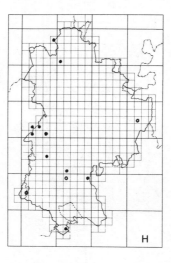

A **Smooth Sow-thistle**, *Sonchus oleraceus*. Waste places

B **Prickly Sow-thistle**, *Sonchus asper*. Waste places

C *Hieracium perpropinquum*. Heaths

D *Hieracium strumosum*. Rough grass-land and woodland borders

E *Hieracium umbellatum*. Heaths

F **Mouse-ear Hawkweed**, *Pilosella officinarum* (*Hieracium pilosella*). Dry banks

G **Beaked Hawk's-beard**, *Crepis vesicaria* subsp. *taraxacifolia*. Rough pastures

H **Rough Hawk's-beard**, *Crepis biennis*. Rough pastures

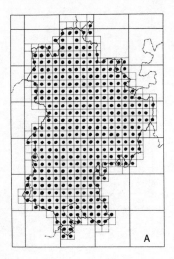

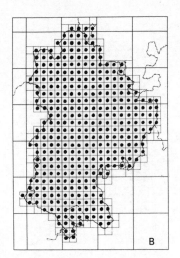

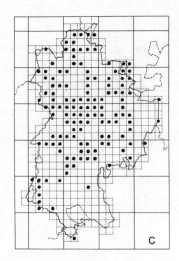

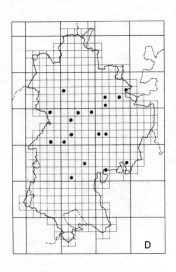

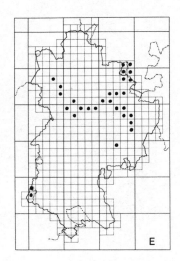

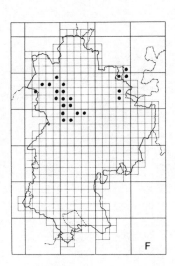

A **Smooth Hawk's-beard**, *Crepis capillaris*. Pastures

B **Dandelion**, *Taraxacum officinale.* Pastures

C **Water-plantain**, *Alisma plantago-aquatica*. Wet places

D **Narrow-leaved Water-plantain**, *Alisma lanceolatum*. Riversides and flooded pits

E **Arrowhead**, *Sagittaria sagittifolia*. Rivers

F **Flowering-rush**, *Butomus umbellatus*. Riversides

G **Canadian Waterweed**, *Elodea canadensis*. Rivers and ponds

H *Lagarosiphon major*. Flooded pits

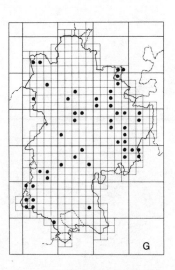

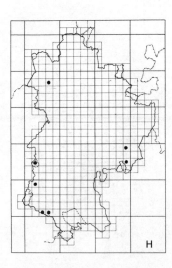

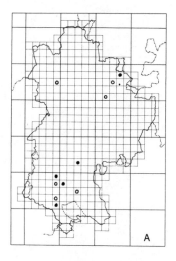

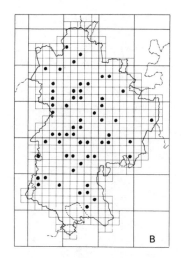

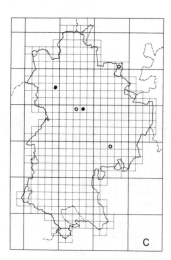

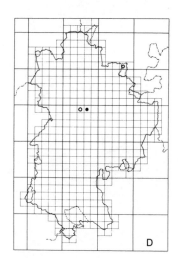

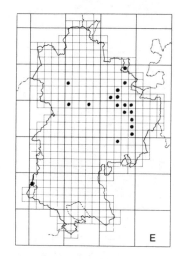

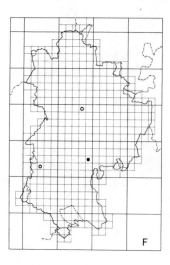

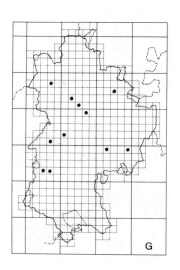

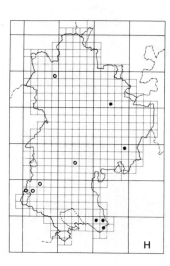

A **Marsh Arrowgrass**, *Triglochin palustris*. Marshes

B **Broad-leaved Pondweed**, *Potamogeton natans*. Still water

C **Shining Pondweed**, *Potamogeton lucens*. Rivers

D **Long-stalked Pondweed**, *Potamogeton praelongus*. Rivers

E **Perfoliate Pondweed**, *Potamogeton perfoliatus*. Rivers

F **Flat-stalked Pondweed**, *Potamogeton friesii*. Lakes

G **Lesser Pondweed**, *Potamogeton pusillus*. Rivers and flooded pits

H **Small Pondweed**, *Potamogeton berchtoldii*. Ponds and rivers

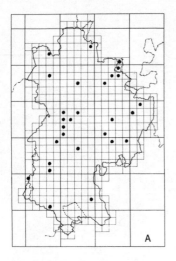

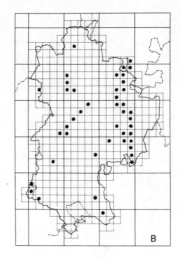

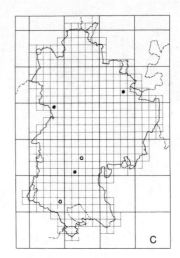

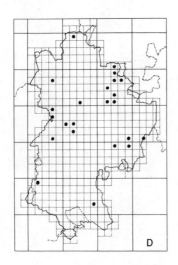

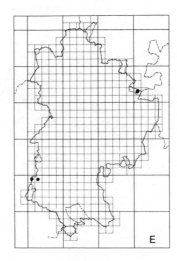

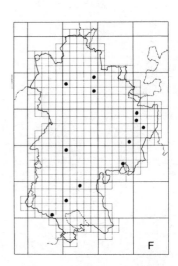

A **Curled Pondweed**, *Potamogeton crispus*. Ponds, lakes and rivers

B **Fennel Pondweed**, *Potamogeton pectinatus*. Flooded pits and rivers

C **Opposite-leaved Pondweed**, *Groenlandia densa* (*Potamogeton densus*). Ponds and ditches

D **Horned Pondweed**, *Zannichellia palustris*. Ponds and ditches

E **Lily-of-the-valley**, *Convallaria majalis*. Woods

F **Star-of-Bethlehem**, *Ornithogalum umbellatum*. Rough grassland and roadside verges

G **Spiked Star-of-Bethlehem**, *Ornithogalum pyrenaicum*. Woods and hedgerows

H **Bluebell**, *Endymion non-scriptus*. Woods

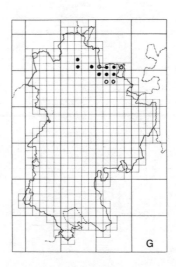

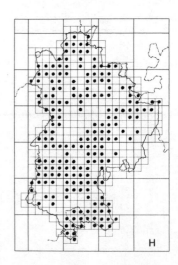

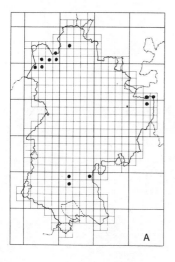

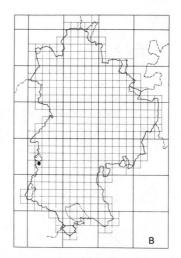

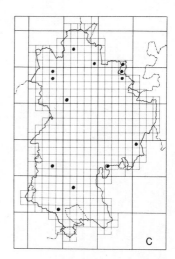

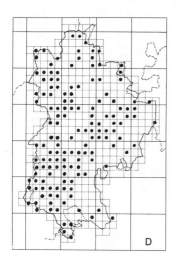

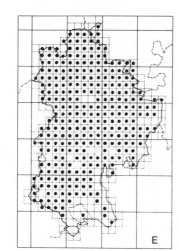

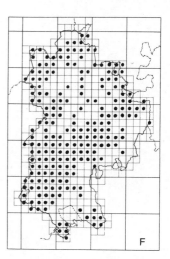

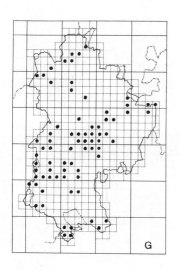

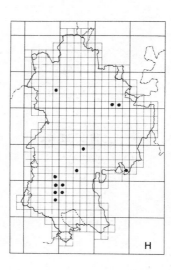

A **Herb-Paris**, *Paris quadrifolia*. Woods

B **Heath Rush**, *Juncus squarrosus*. Heaths

C **Round-fruited Rush**, *Juncus compressus*. Wet pastures

D **Toad Rush**, *Juncus bufonius*. Sides of ponds

E **Hard Rush**, *Juncus inflexus*. Badly drained pastures

F **Soft Rush**, *Juncus effusus*. Marshes

G **Compact Rush**, *Juncus subuliflorus* (*J. conglomeratus*). Wet woods

H **Blunt-fruited Rush**, *Juncus sub-nodulosus*. Marshes

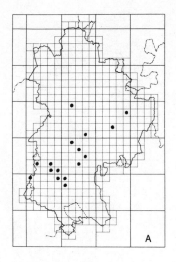

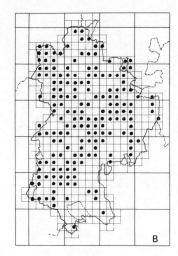

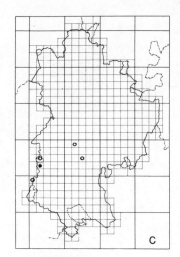

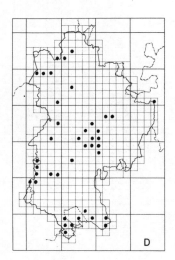

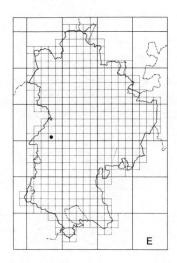

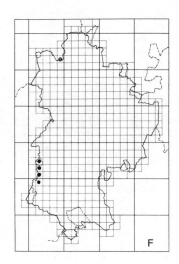

A **Sharp-fruited Rush**, *Juncus acuti-florus*. Marshes

B **Jointed Rush**, *Juncus articulatus*. Marshes

C **Bulbous Rush**, *Juncus bulbosus*. Ponds

D **Hairy Wood-rush**, *Luzula pilosa*. Woods

E **Southern Wood-rush**, *Luzula forsteri*. Woods

F **Great Wood-rush**, *Luzula sylvatica*. Wet woods

G **Field Wood-rush**, *Luzula campestris*. Pastures

H **Heath Wood-rush**, *Luzula multi-flora*. Heaths

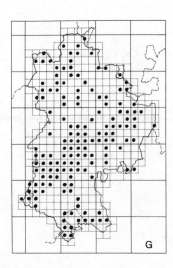

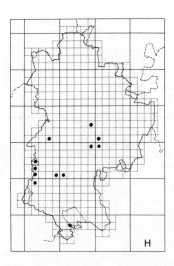

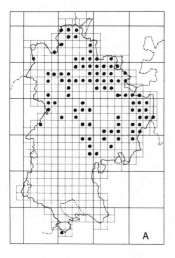

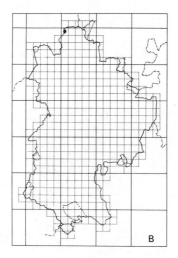

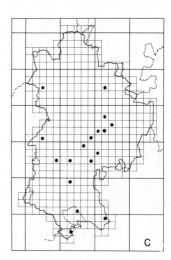

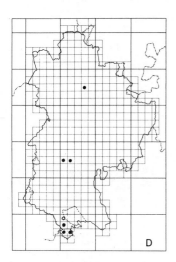

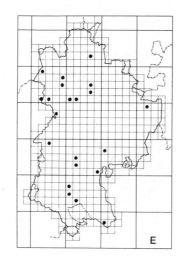

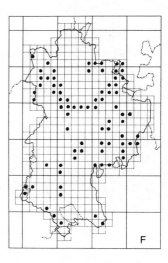

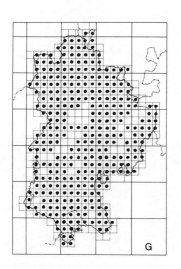

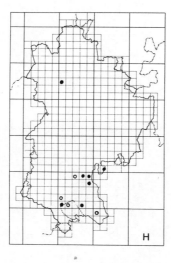

A **Wild Onion**, *Allium vineale*. Road-sides

B **Field Garlic**, *Allium oleraceum*. Rough pastures

C **Ramsons**, *Allium ursinum*. Woods

D **Wild Daffodil**, *Narcissus pseudo-narcissus*. Woods

E **Stinking Iris**, *Iris foetidissima*. Woods

F **Yellow Iris**, *Iris pseudacorus*. Wet places

G **Black Bryony**, *Tamus communis*. Hedgerows

H **White Helleborine**, *Cephalanthera damasonium*. Woods

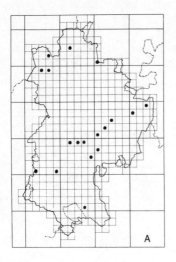

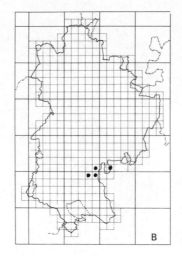

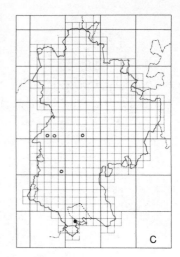

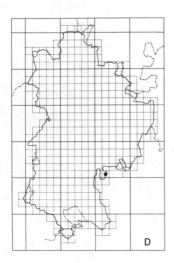

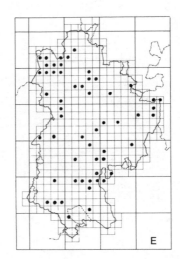

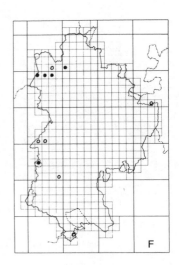

A **Broad-leaved Helleborine**, *Epipactis helleborine*. Woods

B **Green-flowered Helleborine**, *Epipactis phyllanthes*. Woods

C **Violet Helleborine**, *Epipactis purpurata*. Woods

D **Autumn Lady's-tresses**, *Spiranthes spiralis*. Chalk downland

E **Common Twayblade**, *Listera ovata*. Woods and chalk downland

F **Bird's-nest Orchid**, *Neottia nidus-avis*. Woods

G **Musk Orchid**, *Herminium monorchis*. Chalk downland

H **Frog Orchid**, *Coeloglossum viride*. Chalk downland

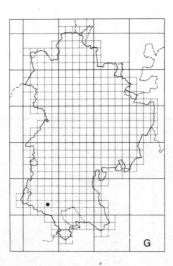

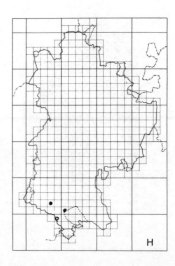

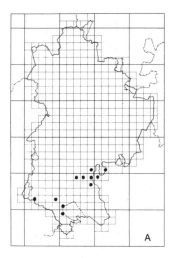

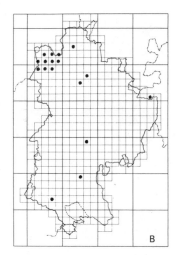

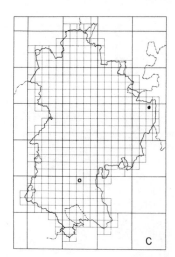

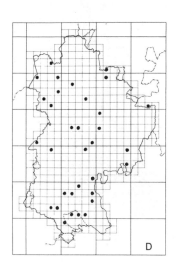

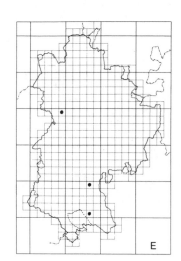

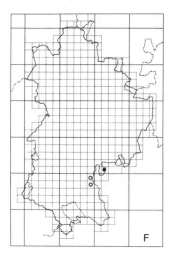

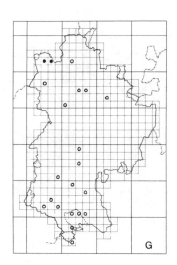

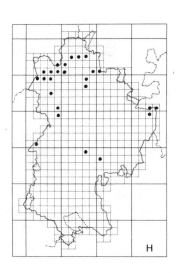

A **Fragrant Orchid**, *Gymnadenia conopsea*. Chalk downland

B **Greater Butterfly-orchid**, *Platanthera chlorantha*. Woods

C **Lesser Butterfly-orchid**, *Platanthera bifolia*. Woods

D **Bee Orchid**, *Ophrys apifera*. Calcareous pastures

E **Fly Orchid**, *Ophrys insectifera*. Woods

F **Burnt Orchid**, *Orchis ustulata*. Chalk downland

G **Green-winged Orchid**, *Orchis morio*. Pastures

H **Early-purple Orchid**, *Orchis mascula*. Woods

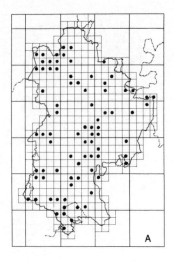

A

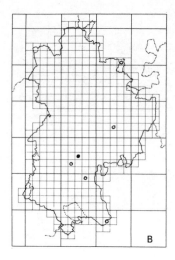

B

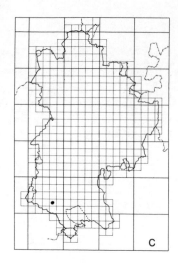

C

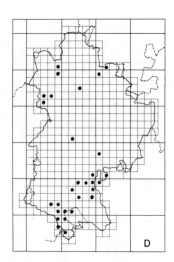

D

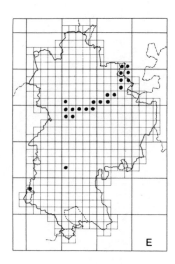

E

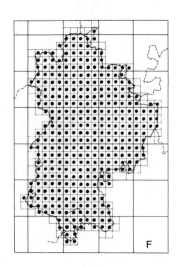

F

A **Common Spotted-orchid**, *Dactylorhiza fuchsii* (*Dactlyorchis f.*). Woodland rides and pastures

B **Southern Marsh-orchid**, *Dactylorhiza praetermissa* (*Dactylorchis p.*). Marshes

C **Man Orchid**, *Aceras anthropophorum*. Chalk downland

D **Pyramidal Orchid**, *Anacamptis pyramidalis*. Calcareous pastures

E **Sweet-flag**, *Acorus calamus*. Riversides

F **Lords-and-Ladies**, *Arum maculatum*. Woods and hedgerows

G **Ivy-leaved Duckweed**, *Lemna trisulca*. Ponds

H **Common Duckweed**, *Lemna minor*. Still water

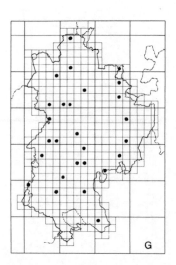

G

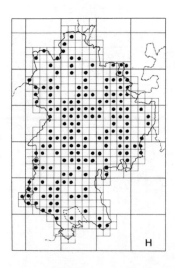

H

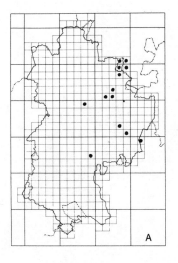

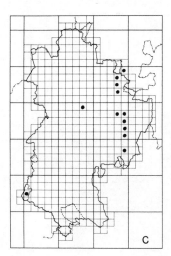

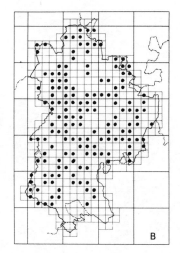

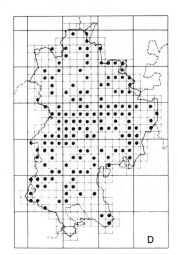

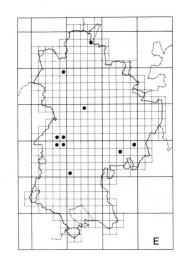

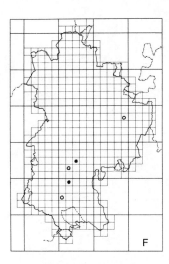

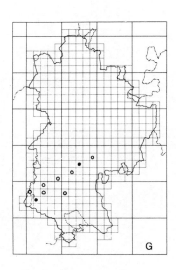

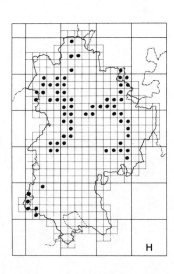

A **Fat Duckweed**, *Lemna gibba*. Ponds and ditches

B **Branched Bur-reed**, *Sparganium erectum*. Wet places

C **Unbranched Bur-reed**, *Sparganium emersum* (*S. simplex*). Rivers

D **Bulrush**, *Typha latifolia*. Lakes and flooded pits

E **Lesser Bulrush**, *Typha angustifolia*. Flooded pits

F **Common Cottongrass**, *Eriophorum angustifolium*. Marshes

G **Wood Club-rush**, *Scirpus sylvaticus*. Wet shady places

H **Common Club-rush**, *Scirpus lacustris*. Rivers and flooded pits

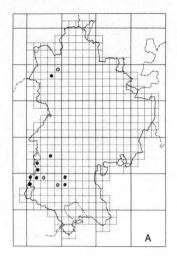

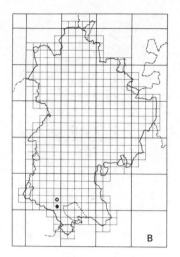

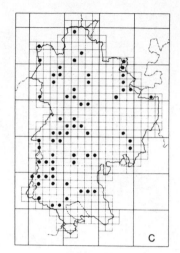

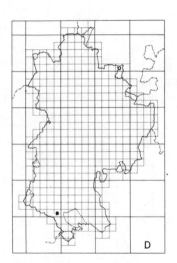

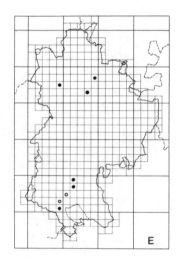

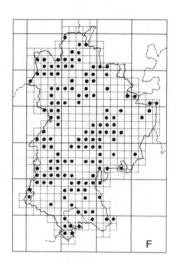

A **Bristle Club-rush**, *Scirpus setaceus*. Wet pastures

B **Flat-sedge**, *Blysmus compressus*. Marshes

C **Common Spike-rush**, *Eleocharis palustris*. Marshes and sides of ponds

D **Slender Spike-rush**, *Eleocharis uniglumis*. Marshes

E **Distant Sedge**, *Carex distans*. Wet pastures

F **Wood-sedge**, *Carex sylvatica*. Woods

G **Cyperus Sedge**, *Carex pseudo-cyperus*. Sides of ponds and lakes

H **Bottle Sedge**, *Carex rostrata*. Marshes and sides of ponds

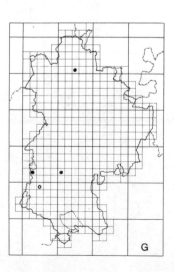

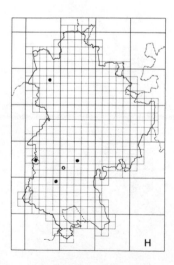

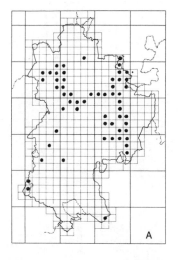

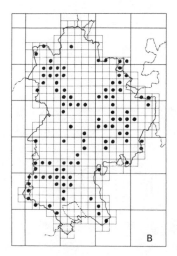

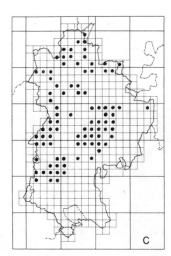

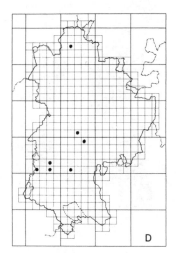

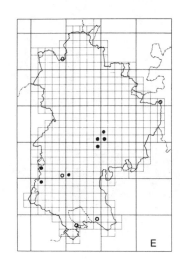

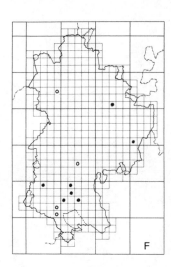

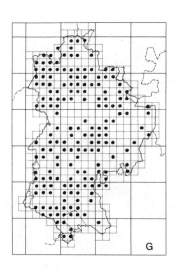

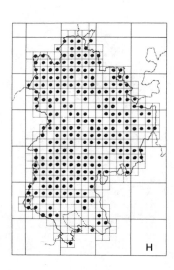

A **Greater Pond-sedge**, *Carex riparia.* Riversides

B **Lesser Pond-sedge**, *Carex acutiformis.* Riversides and marshes

C **Pendulous Sedge**, *Carex pendula.* Wet woods

D **Thin-spiked Wood-sedge**, *Carex strigosa.* Wet woods

E **Pale Sedge**, *Carex pallescens.* Woods

F **Carnation Sedge**, *Carex panicea.* Marshes

G **Glaucous Sedge**, *Carex flacca.* Pastures

H **Hairy Sedge**, *Carex hirta.* Marshes

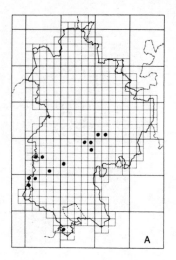

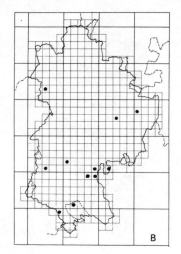

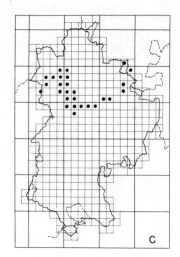

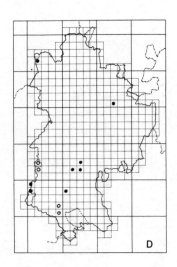

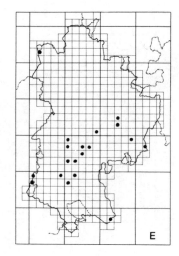

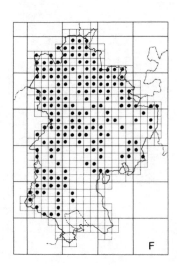

A **Pill Sedge**, *Carex pilulifera*. Heaths

B **Spring-sedge**, *Carex caryophyllea*. Calcareous pastures

C **Slender Tufted-sedge**, *Carex acuta*. Riversides

D **Common Sedge**, *Carex nigra*. Marshes

E **Greater Tussock-sedge**, *Carex paniculata*. Marshes

F **False Fox-sedge**, *Carex otrubae*. Sides of rivers and ditches

G **Spiked Sedge**, *Carex spicata*. Hedgebanks and calcareous pastures

H **Prickly Sedge**, *Carex muricata* (*C. pairaei*). Hedgebanks

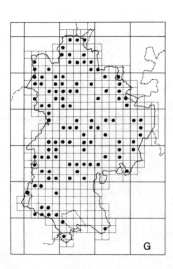

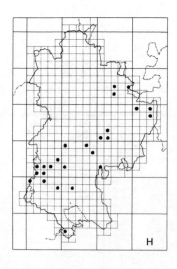

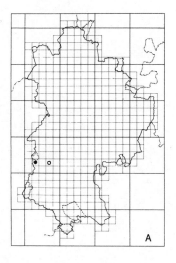

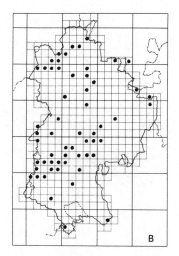

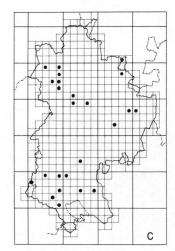

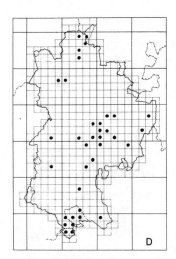

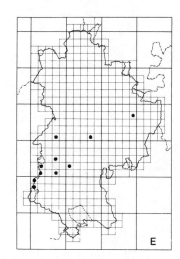

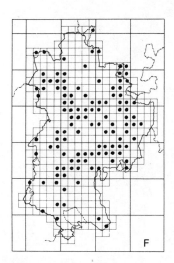

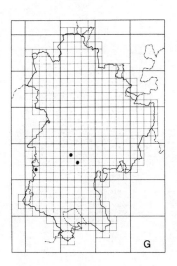

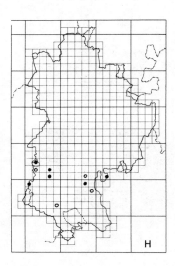

A **Star Sedge**, *Carex echinata.* Wet heathland

B **Remote Sedge**, *Carex remota.* Stream-banks and woodland rides

C **Brown Sedge**, *Carex disticha.* Marshes

D **Grey Sedge**, *Carex divulsa,* Hedge-banks

E **Oval Sedge**, *Carex ovalis.* Marshes

F **Common Reed**, *Phragmites communis.* Wet places

G **Purple Moor-grass**, *Molinia caerulea.* Wet heaths

H **Heath-grass**, *Sieglingia decumbens.* Heaths

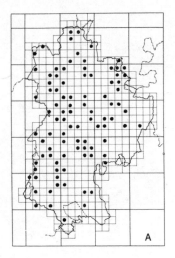

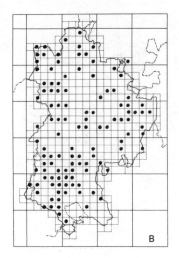

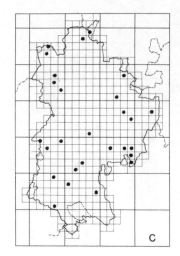

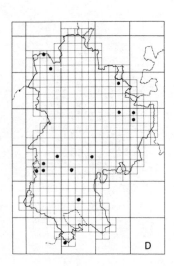

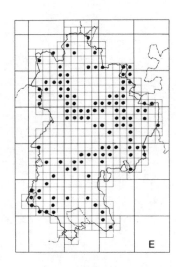

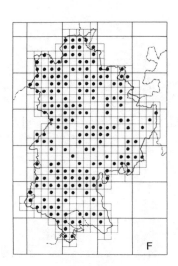

A **Floating Sweet-grass**, *Glyceria fluitans*. Ponds and wet ditches

B **Plicate Sweet-grass**, *Glyceria plicata*. Ponds and wet ditches

C *Glyceria × pedicellata (G. fluitans × plicata)*. Ponds and wet ditches

D **Small Sweet-grass**, *Glyceria declinata*. Sides of ponds

E **Reed Sweet-grass**, *Glyceria maxima*. Sides of lakes and rivers

F **Meadow Fescue**, *Festuca pratensis*. Pastures

G **Tall Fescue**, *Festuca arundinacea*. Roadside verges

H **Giant Fescue**, *Festuca gigantea*. Woods

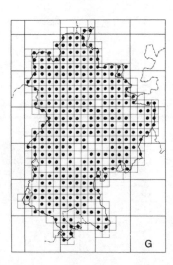

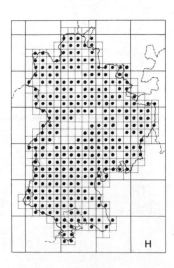

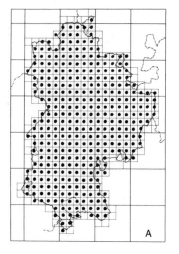

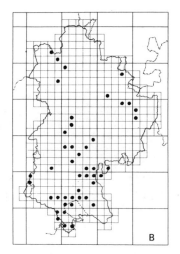

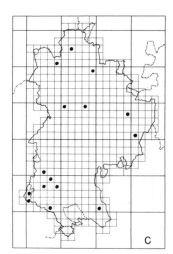

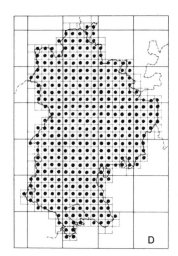

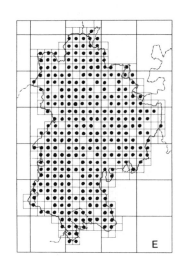

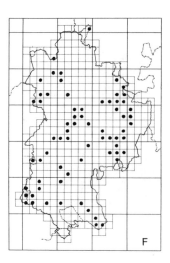

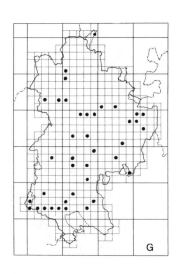

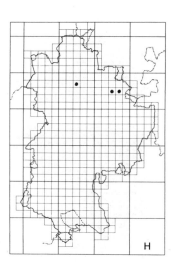

A **Red Fescue**, *Festuca rubra*. Pastures and dry banks

B **Sheep's-fescue**, *Festuca ovina* (including *F. tenuifolia*). Pastures

C × *Festulolium loliaceum* (*Festuca pratensis* × *Lolium perenne*). Pastures

D **Perennial Rye-grass**, *Lolium perenne*. Pastures and waste places

E **Italian Rye-grass**, *Lolium multiflorum*. Pastures and waste places, often sown

F **Squirreltail Fescue**, *Vulpia bromoides*. Bare ground

G **Rat's-tail Fescue**, *Vulpia myuros*. Bare ground

H **Reflexed Saltmarsh-grass**, *Puccinellia distans*. Roadside verges

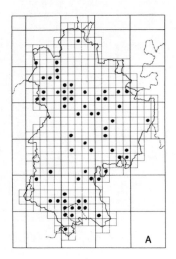

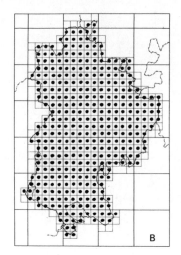

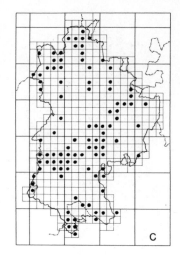

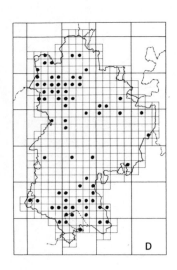

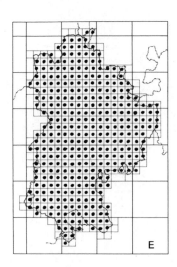

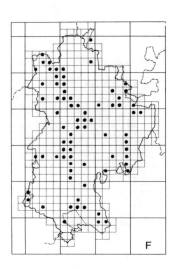

A **Fern-grass**, *Catapodium rigidum*. Bare ground

B **Annual Meadow-grass**, *Poa annua*. Ubiquitous

C **Wood Meadow-grass**, *Poa nemoralis*. Woods

D **Flattened Meadow-grass**, *Poa compressa*. Walls and bare ground

E **Smooth Meadow-grass**, *Poa pratensis*. Pastures

F **Narrow-leaved Meadow-grass**, *Poa angustifolia*. Railway banks

G **Rough Meadow-grass**, *Poa trivialis*. Woods and pastures

H **Whorl-grass**, *Catabrosa aquatica*. Wet places

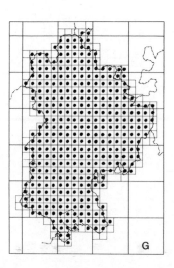

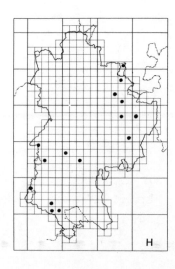

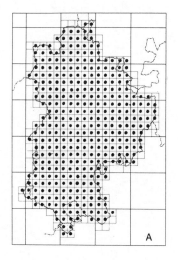

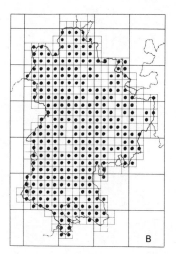

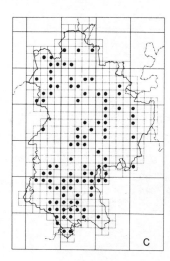

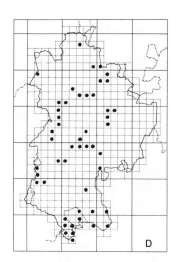

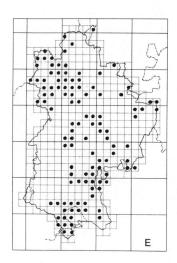

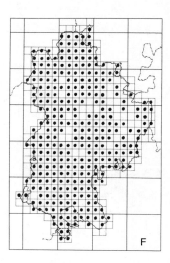

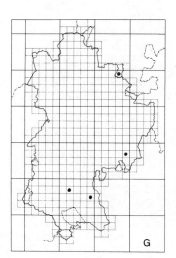

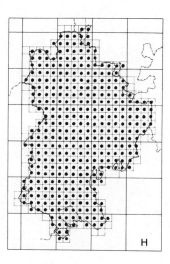

A **Cock's-foot**, *Dactylis glomerata*. Pastures and waste places

B **Crested Dog's-tail**, *Cynosurus cristatus*. Pastures

C **Quaking-grass**, *Briza media*. Old pastures

D **Wood Melick**, *Melica uniflora*. Woods

E **Upright Brome**, *Bromus erectus*. Calcareous pastures

F **Hairy-Brome**, *Bromus ramosus*. Woods and hedgerows

G **Hungarian Brome**, *Bromus inermis*. Waste places

H **Barren Brome**, *Bromus sterilis*. Pastures and waste places

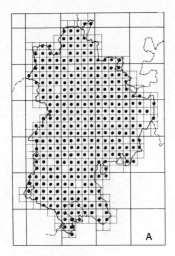

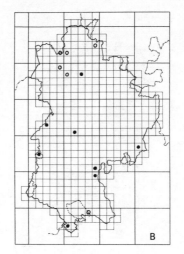

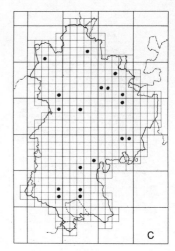

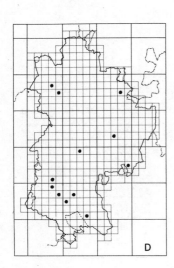

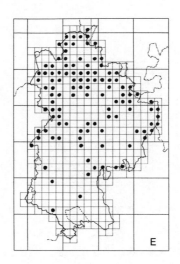

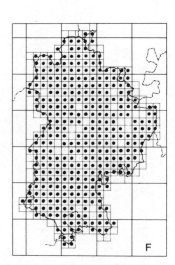

A **Soft-brome**, *Bromus mollis*. Pastures and waste places

B **Lesser Soft-brome**, *Bromus thominii*. Pastures

C **Slender Soft-brome**, *Bromus lepidus*. Roadside verges and waste places

D **Smooth Brome**, *Bromus racemosus*. Old pastures

E **Meadow Brome**, *Bromus commutatus*. Pastures

F **False Brome**, *Brachypodium sylvaticum*. Woods and hedgerows

G **Tor-grass**, *Brachypodium pinnatum*. Calcareous pastures and wood borders

H **Bearded Couch**, *Agropyron caninum*. Woods

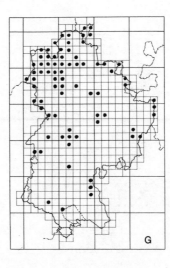

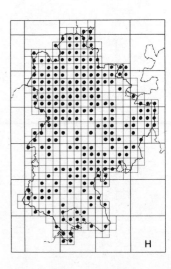

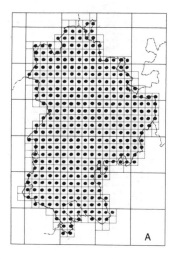

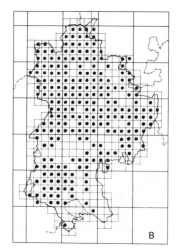

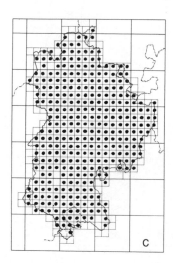

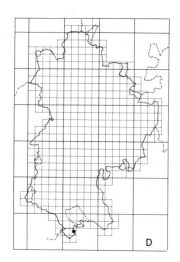

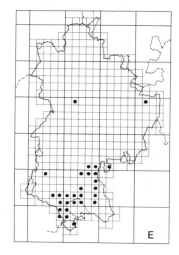

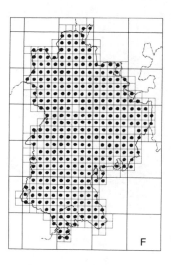

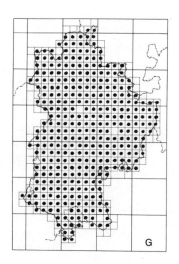

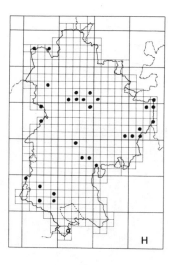

A **Common Couch**, *Agropyron repens*. Arable land and waste places

B **Meadow Barley**, *Hordeum secalinum*. Pastures

C **Wall Barley**, *Hordeum murinum*. Roadsides

D **Wood Barley**, *Hordelymus europaeus*. Woods

E **Crested Hair-grass**, *Koeleria cristata* (*K. gracilis*). Calcareous pastures

F **Yellow Oat-grass**, *Trisetum flavescens*. Pastures

G **Wild-oat**, *Avena fatua*. Arable land

H **Winter Wild-oat**, *Avena ludoviciana*. Arable land

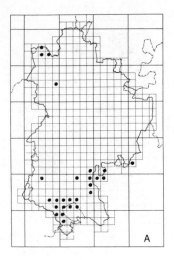

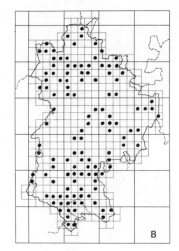

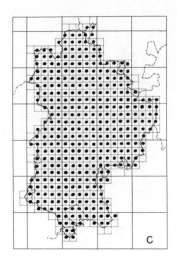

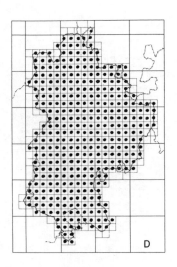

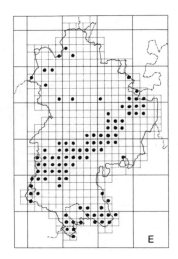

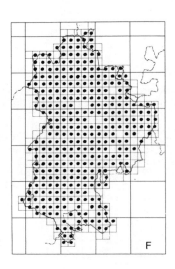

A **Meadow Oat-grass**, *Helictotrichon pratense*. Calcareous pastures

B **Downy Oat-grass**, *Helictotrichon pubescens*. Pastures

C **False Oat-grass**, *Arrhenatherum elatius*. Roadside verges and waste places

D **Yorkshire-fog**, *Holcus lanatus*. Pastures

E **Creeping Soft-grass**, *Holcus mollis*. Wood verges and acid pastures

F **Tufted Hair-grass**, *Deschampsia cespitosa*. Damp pastures and woodland

G **Wavy Hair-grass**, *Deschampsia flexuosa*. Heaths

H **Early Hair-grass**, *Aira praecox*. Heaths

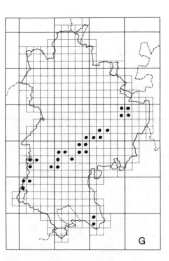

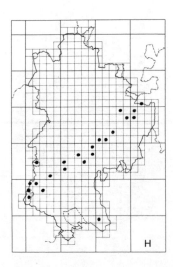

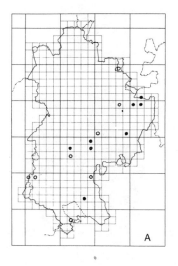

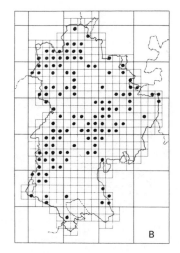

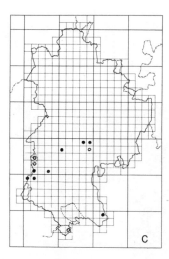

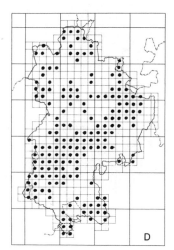

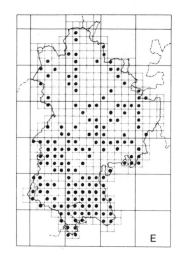

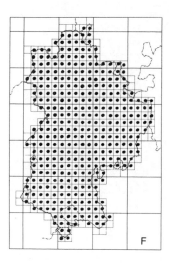

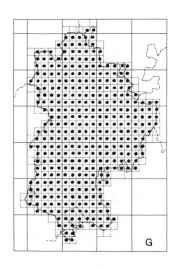

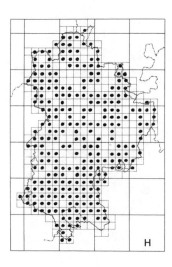

A **Silver Hair-grass**, *Aira caryophyllea*. Dry banks

B **Wood Small-reed**, *Calamagrostis epigejos*. Rough grassland and wood borders

C **Brown Bent**, *Agrostis canina*. Wet heaths

D **Common Bent**, *Agrostis tenuis*. Pastures

E **Black Bent**, *Agrostis gigantea*. Arable land

F **Creeping Bent**, *Agrostis stolonifera*. Pastures and waste places

G **Smaller Cat's-tail**, *Phleum bertolonii* (*P. nodosum*). Pastures

H **Timothy**, *Phleum pratense*. Arable land and rough pastures

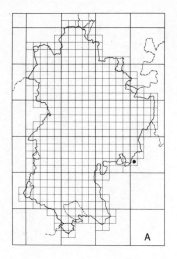

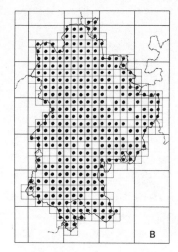

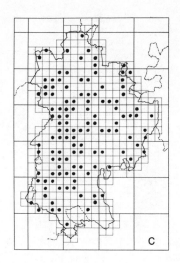

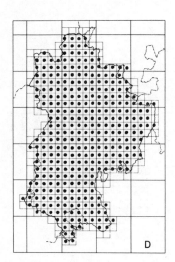

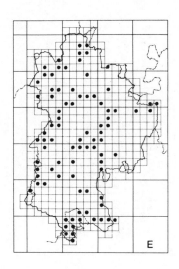

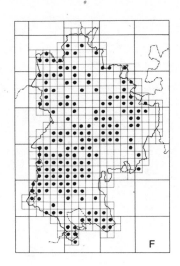

A **Purple-stem Cat's-tail**, *Phleum phleoides*. Dry banks

B **Black-grass**, *Alopecurus myosuroides*. Arable land

C **Marsh Foxtail**, *Alopecurus geniculatus*. Wet places

D **Meadow Foxtail**, *Alopecurus pratensis*. Pastures

E **Wood Millet**, *Milium effusum*. Woods

F **Sweet Vernal-grass**, *Anthoxanthum odoratum*. Pastures

G **Reed Canary-grass**, *Phalaris arundinacea*. Sides of lakes and rivers

H **Canary-grass**, *Phalaris canariensis*. Waste places

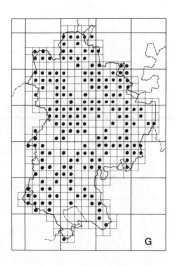

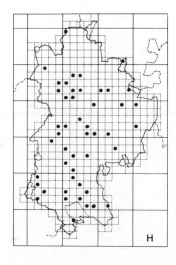

SPECIES FOR WHICH MAPS ARE NOT PROVIDED

For notes on arrangement and explanation of symbols used, see page 22.

LYCOPODIACEAE
Stag's-horn Clubmoss, *Lycopodium clavatum*. Last recorded 1907.
Marsh C., *L. inundatum*. Wet heaths (93G).

EQUISETACEAE (p. 23)
Rough Horsetail, *Equisetum hyemale*. Last recorded 1798.
Wood H., *E. sylvaticum*. Last recorded 1798.

ASPIDIACEAE (p. 24)
Scaly Male-fern, *Dryopteris pseudomas (D. borreri)*. Woods (92J, 96Q, 01C, 11J).

THELYPTERIDACEAE (p. 25)
Lemon-scented Fern, *Thelypteris limbosperma (T. oreopteris)*. Heathy woods (93G).
Marsh F., *T. palustris*. Last recorded 1798.
Limestone F., *Gymnocarpium robertianum (G. obtusifolium)*. Walls (02S, 03I).

‡ **Water Fern**, *Azolla filiculoides* (AZOLLACEAE). Introduced into ponds: 02S, 04E.

OPHIOGLOSSACEAE (p. 25)
Moonwort, *Botrychium lunaria*. Last recorded 1798.

Larch, *Larix decidua* (PINACEAE). A planted tree only.

Juniper, *Juniperus communis* (CUPRESSACEAE). Last recorded 1889.

Yew, *Taxus baccata* (TAXACEAE). A planted tree only.

RANUNCULACEAE (p. 25)
‡ **Monk's-hood**, *Aconitum napellus*. 05K, 16F.
Pheasant's-eye, *Adonis annua*. Arable fields: 13F.
‡ **Blue Anemone**, *Anemone apennina* (03G).
Yellow A., *A. ranunculoides*. Last recorded c. 1890.
Anemone coronaria. Only record 1884.
Columbine, *Aquilegia vulgaris*. Last recorded as a native woodland species 1930, now a garden escape on most refuse tips.
‡ **Larkspur**, *Delphinium ambiguum (D. gayanum)*. 05FG, 12F (02J).
‡ **Winter Aconite**, *Eranthis hyemalis*. Naturalised and usually near to houses: 92S, 95Y, 96R, 02DVW, 03A, 05A, 15G.
Mousetail, *Myosurus minimus*. Arable fields (02F).
Greater Spearwort, *Ranunculus lingua*. Last recorded 1881 but status not known.

BERBERIDACEAE (p. 28)
‡ **Oregon Grape**, *Mahonia aquifolium*. Planted in woods. Recorded for 30 tetrads.

CERATOPHYLLACEAE (p. 29)
Soft Hornwort, *Ceratophyllum submersum*. Only record 1887.

PAPAVERACEAE (p. 29)
§ *Argemone mexicana*.
§ *Glaucium corniculatum*.

FUMARIACEAE (p. 30)
‡ **Yellow Corydalis**, *Corydalis lutea*. On walls, usually near houses: 92Q, 93LW, 95L, 01JN, 03MPX, 06M, 13G, 14M, 15G.
‡ *Corydalis solida*. 93N, 01D, 02B.
* **Tall Ramping-fumitory**, *Fumaria bastardii*. (03N).
* **Common R.**, *F. muralis* subsp. *boraei*. 95Y.
Fine-leaved Fumitory, *F. parviflora*. Arable fields (12E).
Fumaria densiflora × *F. officinalis*. 02A.

CRUCIFERAE (p. 30)
Small Alison, *Alyssum alyssoides*. Railway bank: 03H, last seen 1969.
Medium-flowered Winter-cress, *Barbarea intermedia*. Waste ground: 12B, 15B.
American W., *B. verna*. Waste ground: 96K.
Berteroa incana. Last recorded 1884.
* **Chinese Mustard**, *Brassica juncea*. (03H, 14X, 16Q).
Brassica elongata. Only record 1897.
§ *B. griquana*, *B. tournefortii*.
* **Warty Cabbage**, *Bunias orientalis*. 03U, 13X, 04A (02H).
* *Bunias erucago*. (02W, 04P).
* **Gold-of-pleasure**, *Camelina sativa*. 92X, 02X, 12F, 24E.
* *Camelina microcarpa*. (03H).
Wallflower, *Cheiranthus cheri*. Last recorded 1846.
Danish Scurvygrass, *Cochlearia danica*. Frequent on railway ballast 1945–1955.
Round-podded Whitlowgrass, *Erophila spathulata*. Bare ground: 03M, appearing regularly.
* *Eruca sativa*. 92I, 05F.
* *Erucaria hispanica*. (02J).
Hairy Rocket, *Erucastrum gallicum*. Waste ground: 13X, appearing regularly.
‡ **Dame's-violet**, *Hesperis matronalis*. Recorded for 33 tetrads.
§ *Hirschfeldia incana*.
‡ **Garden Candytuft**, *Iberis umbellata*. 05G, 12F, (03J).
Woad, *Isatis tinctoria*. Last recorded 1695.
Dittander, *Lepidium latifolium*. Waste places: 02M.
‡ **Garden Cress**, *Lepidium sativum*. 92I, 02J, 03H, 05G, 12F, 24E.
Lepidium perfoliatum. Only record 1923.
§ *L. divaricatum*, *L. hyssopifolium*. *L. virginicum*.
‡ **Sweet Alison**, *Lobularia maritima*. 92U, 02B, 04BM, 05FG, 12F.
‡ **Honesty**, *Lunaria annua*. 92J, 93FST, 96V, 13N.
Stock, '*Malcolmia africana*'. Only record 1935.
* *Neslia paniculata*. 05G.
‡ **Garden Radish**, *Raphanus sativus*. 12F.
* **Steppe Cabbage**, *Rapistrum perenne*. (92C, 14E).
* **Bastard C.**, *R. rugosum*. Recorded for 22 tetrads.
Rorippa microphylla × *R. nasturtium-aquaticum*. 16Q (96V).
§ **London-rocket**, *Sisymbrium irio*.
§ **False London-rocket**, *S. loeselii*. 12F (02J).
§ *Sisymbrium erysimoides*.
§ *Vella annua*.

RESEDACEAE (p. 35)
White Mignonette, *Reseda alba*. Roadsides (93Z, 15P). Status not known.

VIOLACEAE (p. 35)
Wild Pansy, *Viola tricolor*. Arable land: 03GH, appearing regularly.
Viola hirta subsp. *calcarea*. Chalk downland: 02Z.
V. canina × *V. riviniana*. 11J.
V. hirta × *V. odorata*. 12F (03H, 04K).

GUTTIFERAE (p. 36)
‡ **Tutsan**, *Hypericum androsaemum*. Naturalised: 93LR.
‡ **Rose-of-Sharon**, *H. calycinum*. Naturalised: 93LRV.
Marsh St. John's-wort, *H. elodes*. Last recorded 1798.
Stinking Tutsan, *H. hircinum*. Last recorded c. 1900.
Pale St. John's-wort, *H. montanum*. Last recorded c. 1921 but status not known.
Hypericum maculatum subsp. *maculatum*. Hedgebanks: 93I

CARYOPHYLLACEAE (p. 37)
Corncockle, *Agrostemma githago*. Arable fields, frequent until about 1950. Last recorded c. 1955.
‡ **Snow-in-Summer**, *Cerastium tomentosum*. Recorded for 21 tetrads.
‡ **Sweet-William**, *Dianthus barbatus*. (02J).
Maiden Pink, *D. deltoides*. Last recorded 1798.
Upright Chickweed, *Moenchia erecta*. Heaths. Last recorded 1930.
Childling Pink, *Petrorhagia nanteuilii (Kohlrauschia prolifera)*. Sandy banks: 24E, well established but status uncertain.
Knotted Pearlwort, *Sagina nodosa*. Damp pastures. Last recorded 1926.
Forked Catchfly, *Silene dichotoma*. (02U).
‡ **Small-flowered C.**, *S. gallica (S. anglica)*. 02F.
‡ *Silene coeli-rosa*. (02J).
‡ *S. pendula*. (05G).
§ *S. nocturna*.
Lesser Chickweed, *Stellaria pallida (S. apetala)*. Dry pastures (03IN).
Marsh Stitchwort, *S. palustris*. Marshes (03M). Last seen c. 1968.
Stellaria neglecta is of doubtful occurrence and previous records probably in error.
* **Cowherb**, *Vaccaria pyramidata*. 02E (02J).

ILLECEBRACEAE (p. 40)
§ *Herniaria cinerea, H. hirsuta*.

PORTULACACEAE (p. 41)
‡ **Pink Purslane**, *Montia sibirica (Claytonia alsinoides)*. (93N).

AIZOACEAE
§ *Mesembryanthemum crystallinum*.
§ *Galenia africana*.

AMARANTHACEAE
§ *Alternanthera peploides*.
‡ **Love-lies-bleeding**, *Amaranthus caudatus*. 05F (02J, 12F).
* *Amaranthus blitoides*. (02J).
* *A. retroflexus*. 92I, 03G, 13H.
§ *A. albus, A. deflexus, A. dinteri, A. hybridus* subsp. *hybridus, A. hybridus* subsp. *incurvatus, A. macrocarpus, A. mitchellii, A. quitensis, A. spinosus, A. thunbergii, A. viridis*.

CHENOPODIACEAE (p. 41)
‡ **Garden Orache**, *Atriplex hortensis*. 94U, 02Q, 04PU, 05FG, 12F, 14Q, 24I.
‡ *Atriplex nitens*. (03X, 05G).
§ *A. eardleyae, A. muelleri, A. semibaccata, A. suberecta*.
§ *Bassia birchii*.
* **Strawberry Blite**, *Chenopodium capitatum*. (01Z).
Oak-leaved Goosefoot, *C. glaucum*. Last recorded 1802.
§ *Chenopodium ambrosioides, C. auricomiforme, C. bernburgense, C. carinatum, C. cristatum, C. giganteum, C. hircinum, C. macrospermum, C. nitrariaceum, C. praetericola, C. probstii, C. pumilio, C. schraderianum, C. strictum (C. striatum), C. urbicum, C. vulvaria*.
§ *Kochia scoparia (K. densiflora), K. sieversiana*.
§ *Monolepis nutalliana*.
* *Salsola pestiver*. 02B (02Q, 14K).
§ *Scleroblitum atriciplinum*.

§ *Phytolacca octandra* (PHYTOLACCACEAE).

TILIACEAE (p. 42)
Lime, *Tilia* × *vulgaris*. Occurs throughout the county as a planted tree.
Large-leaved Lime, *T. platyphyllos*. A planted tree.
§ *Triumfetta annua*.

MALVACEAE (p. 42)
§ *Abutilon theophrasti*.
‡ **Hollyhock**, *Althaea rosea*. 05FG, 12F, (02J).
§ *Hibiscus trionum*.
§ *Lavatera cretica, L. plebeia*.
‡ *L. thuringiaca*. (24P).
‡ *L. trimestris*. 15G (13C). Occurs also as a wool alien.
‡ *Malva alcea*. (02J).
§ *M. nicaeensis, M. parviflora, M. pusilla, M. verticillata*.
§ *Malvastrum coromandelianum, M. multicaule, M. spicatum, M. peruvianum*.
§ *Pavonia urens*.
§ *Sida cordifolia, S. glomerata*.
§ *Urocarpidium shepardae*.

LINACEAE (p. 42)
* **Flax**, *Linum usitatissimum*. 92I, 93U, 01E, 02C, 04MZ, 05G, 06E, 12F, 24E.

GERANIACEAE (p. 43)
§ *Erodium botrys, E. chium, E. ciconium, E. crinitum, E. cygnorum, E. geoides, E. gruinum, E. malachoides, E. moschatum, E. obtusiplicatum, E. stephanianum*.
‡ **French Crane's-bill**, *Geranium endressii*. 93S (03H).
‡ **Shining C.**, *G. lucidum*. 02V, 05AK, 06H, 24J (12B, 14M).
‡ **Dusky C.**, *G. phaeum*. 11I, long established.
‡ **Bloody C.**, *G. sanguineum*. 03J.
Geranium endressii × *versicolor*.
§ *Monsonia angustifolia, M. brevirostrata*.

OXALIDACEAE (p. 44)
‡ *Oxalis corniculata*. 02Q, 13X, 15G.
‡ *O. corymbosa*. 92I, 15AG.
‡ *O. europaea*. 92I, 15G.

ACERACEAE (p. 45)
Norway Maple, *Acer platanoides*. A planted tree, recorded from 15 tetrads.

Horse-chestnut, *Aesculus hippocastanum* (HIPPOCASTANACEAE). Occurs throughout the county as a planted tree.

Box, *Buxus sempervirens* (BUXACEAE). Possibly once native on chalk downland, now planted in parklands.

LEGUMINOSAE (p. 45)
* **Chick Pea**, *Cicer arietinum*. 05G.
‡ **Crown Vetch**, *Coronilla varia*. 04U, long established (02B, 05GJ).
Petty Whin, *Genista anglica*. Last recorded 1875.
§ *Hedysarum spinosissimum*.
‡ **Laburnum**, *Laburnum anagyroides*. 93F, 03J, 12F, 13A, 14I.
* **Yellow Vetchling**, *Lathyrus aphaca*. 23E (02VW).
* **Hairy V.**, *L. hirsutus*. 01Y, 02J.
‡ **Lentil**, *Lens culinaris*. (02J).
‡ **Lupin**, *Lupinus luteus*.
Sickle Medick, *Medicago falcata*. Pastures (04J, 14W, 15U).
§ *Medicago aschersoniana, M. ciliaris, M. laciniata, M. minima, M. polymorpha (M. denticulata, M. hispida), M. preocox, M. truncatula (M. tribuloides)*.
* **Small Melilot**, *Melilotus indica*. 02V, 03GT, 05EV, 14U, 23D.
§ *Melilotus sulcata*.
§ *Psoralea cinerea*.
Acacia, *Robinia pseudoacacia*. A planted tree: 93KLR, 03U.
§ *Scorpiurus muricatus* (including *S. subvillosus*).
§ *Sesbania aculeata*.

‡ **Crimson Clover**, *Trifolium incarnatum*. (02BJ).
§ *Trifolium angustifolium, T. aureum (T. agrarium), T. cernuum, T. constantinopolitanum, T. echinatum, T. glomeratum, T. hirtum, T. lappaceum, T. patens, T. purpureum, T. squamosum, T. resupinatum, T. tomentosum. Trigonella procumbens*. Only record 1912.
* **Yellow Vetch**, *Vicia lutea*. (02J).
Fine-leaved Vetch, *V. tenuifolia*. Railway bank: 03G.
Vicia hybrida. Only record 1884.
* *V. pannonica*. (02J).
§ *V. benghalensis (V. atropurpurea), V. dasycarpa*.

ROSACEAE (p. 51)
§ *Acaena adscendens, A. integerrima, A. novae-zelandiae. Alchemilla xanthochlora*. Pastures (11E).
Geum rivale × G. urbanum. 05R.
Medlar, *Mespilus germanica*. Originally planted: 05R.
Marsh Cinquefoil, *Potentilla palustris*. Marshes (03GM). Last recorded 1969.
‡ **Sulphur C.**, *P. recta*. 15F (02LZ, 03V, 12E).
‡ **Ternate-leaved C.**, *P. norvegica*. (11I).
Potentilla bifurca. Only record 1885.
Trailing Cinquefoil, *P. anglica*. Of doubtful occurrence in the county as previous records may refer to *P. erecta × P. reptans* which often occurs where both parents are present.
Fodder Burnet, *Poterium polygamum*. A relic of cultivation (03H, 06P).
Wild Plum, *Prunus domestica*. Planted frequently near to farms and houses. Recorded for 51 tetrads.
Laurel, *P. laurocerasus*. Planted in parkland woods.
‡ **Peach**, *P. persica*. (02J).
Bird Cherry, *P. padus*. Last recorded c. 1930. Status not known.
Dwarf C., *P. cerasus*. Doubtfully wild in the county. 01C.
Wild Pear, *Pyrus communis*. Hedgerows, in all instances probably planted: 02ABDQ, 03QTU, 05L, 13N.
‡ **Japanese Rose**, *Rosa rugosa*. Hedgerows, often planted: 93T, 02V.
Rosa micrantha. Hedgerows: 01CZ (03V).
For a fuller account of the roses of the county see the Flora.
Swedish Whitebeam, *Sorbus intermedia*. A planted tree: 93Q, 02BR, 04P.
‡ **Garden Bridewort**, *Spiraea × billiardii*. (05G).

The Flora listed 79 microspecies of Bramble (*Rubus* spp.) based almost entirely on visits made to the county by W. C. R. Watson in 1946, 1947 and 1948. Watson found the Clay-with-Flints and those parts of the Lower Greensand not subject to glaciation the most profitable.

CRASSULACEAE (p. 56)
Alternate-leaved Golden-saxifrage, *Chrysosplenium alternifolium*. Only record 1844.
‡ **Reflexed Stonecrop**, *Sedum reflexum*. 02R (02 BI).
‡ *Sedum spurium*. 05P, 24J.
House-leek, *Sempervivum tectorum*. Planted on roofs: 05HJ, 15C.
Grass-of-Parnassus, *Parnassia palustris* (PARNASSIACEAE). Marshes and chalk downland. Last recorded 1925.

DROSERACEAE
Round-leaved Sundew, *Drosera rotundifolia*. Marshes. Last recorded 1942.
Great S., *D. anglica*. Last recorded 1798.

LYTHRACEAE (p. 57)
Grass-poly, *Lythrum hyssopifolia*. Garden path: 15G, origin not known. Occurs also as a wool alien.
§ *Lythrum junceum*.

ONAGRACEAE (p. 57)
‡ *Clarkia elegans*. (02J).
Spear-leaved Willowherb, *Epilobium lanceolatum*. Woods (93H). For details of hybrid willowherbs recorded for the county see the Flora.
§ *Oenothera laciniata, O. sinuata, O. stricta*.
Common Evening-primrose, *Oenothera biennis*. The records in the Flora of *O. biennis* should be referred to *O. erythrosepalum*.

HALORAGACEAE (p. 58)
Alternate Water-milfoil, *Myriophyllum alterniflorum*. Last recorded 1889.
§ *Myriophyllum verrucosum*.

CORNACEAE (p. 59)
Cornelian Cherry, *Cornus mas*. Planted: 92E, 03J.

UMBELLIFERAE (p. 60)
§ *Ammi majus, A. visnaga*.
* **Dill**, *Anethum graveolens*. 04M, 05FG.
Garden Chervil, *Anthriscus cerefolium*. Last recorded 1798.
Wild Celery, *Apium graveolens*. Ditches (04N). Last seen c. 1955.
§ *Apium leptophyllum*.
Thorow-wax, *Bupleurum rotundifolium*. Arable fields (24GP). Last recorded 1943. Later records are in error for the following.
* **False Thorow-wax**, *B. lancifolium*. (02JV).
Greater Bur-parsley, *Caucalis latifolia*. Last recorded c. 1920.
Small B., *C. platycarpos (C. royeni)*. Last recorded c. 1860.
§ *Caucalis melanantha*.
Caraway, *Carum carvi*. Pastures (92V). Last seen 1966. Occurs also as a casual (02J).
Cowbane, *Cicuta virosa*. Last recorded 1798.
* **Coriander**, *Coriandrum sativum*. 03G, 05FG, 12F, 24E.
* **Cuminum**, *Cuminum cyminum*. (02J).
§ *Daucus crinitus, D. glochidiatus*.
Longleaf, *Falcaria vulgaris*. Field borders (95N). Last recorded c. 1960.
‡ **Giant Hogweed**, *Heracleum mantegazzianum*. 93T, long established, 01E, 14I.
Narrow-leaved Water-dropwort, *Oenanthe silaifolia*. Last recorded 1864, the record in Dony (1969) was in error.
River W., *O. fluviatilis*. Rivers (04U, 14L).
Hemlock W., *O. crocata*. Last recorded 1911.
‡ **Garden Parsley**, *Petroselinum crispum*. 24E.
§ *Ridolfia segetum*.
§ *Torilis leptophylla*.

CUCURBITACEAE (p. 64)
‡ **Water Melon**, *Citrullus lanatus*. (02J).
§ *Cucumis myriocarpus*.
‡ **Melon**, *C. melo*. (02J).
‡ **Gourd**, *Cucurbita pepo*. 92I, 02B, 05FG, 12F.
§ *Ecballium elaterium*.

Birthwort, *Aristolochia clematitis* (ARISTOLOCHIACEAE). Last recorded 1881.

EUPHORBIACEAE (p. 64)
‡ **Caper Spurge**, *Euphorbia lathyrus*. 95L, 01J, 02V, 05FG, 12F, 14EU, 15G, 23B.

POLYGONACEAE (p. 65)
‡ **Buckwheat**, *Fagopyrum esculentum*. 92I, 94TZ, 95P, 06B, 12F, 24E.
§ *Fagopyrum tataricum*.
‡ **Russian-vine**, *Polygonum aubertii ('P. baldschuanicum')*. 01D, 13R.

‡ **Giant Knotweed**, *P. sachalinense*. 93T, 15A.
§ *Polygonum patulum, P. plebejum, P. senegalense*.
Rumex tenuifolius, Heaths (92J, 14A).
Docks hybridise readily and the following are recorded:
Rumex conglomeratus × *R. crispus*.
R. conglomeratus × *R. obtusifolius*.
R. conglomeratus × *R. palustris*.
R. crispus × *R. obtusifolius*.
R. crispus × *R. sanguineus*.
R. obtusifolius × *R. sanguineus*.
§ *R. brownii, R. dentatus* subsp. *halacsyi*.

URTICACEAE (p. 67)
‡ **Mind-your-own-business**, *Soleirolia soleirolii*. 93R, 01Z, 14X.
Roman Nettle, *Urtica pilulifera*. Last recorded 1876.
§ *Urtica incisa*.

ULMACEAE (p. 68)
For the purposes of the survey the elms were taken to comprise three species for which maps are provided but for an alternative treatment see the Flora.

CANNABIACEAE (p. 68)
* **Hemp**, *Cannabis sativa*. 02C, 05FG, 12F, 24E.
‡ **Fig**, *Ficus carica* (MORACEAE). 02V, (13U).

London Plane, *Platanus* × *hybrida* (PLANTANACEAE). Occurs rarely as a planted tree.

FAGACEAE (p. 69)
Turkey Oak, *Quercus cerris*. A planted tree. Recorded for 53 tetrads.
Evergreen Oak, *Q. ilex*. Planted, usually near houses. Various introduced species of oak are planted in parkland woods.

SALICACEAE (p. 69)
Balsam Poplar, *Populus gileadensis*. A planted tree: 92E, 93L, 02W, 03U, 13I, 14N.
Poplars, mainly hybrid strains, are planted and form plantations in the Ouse valley.
Creeping Willow, *Salix repens*. Last recorded 1911.
For details of hybrid willows see the Flora.

ERICACEAE (p. 71)
Bell Heather, *Erica cinerea*. Heaths: 14A, presumably accidentally introduced.
Cross-leaved Heath, *Erica tetralix*. Last recorded c. 1880.
Cranberry, *Vaccinium oxycoccos*. Last recorded 1798.
Rhododendron, *Rhododendron ponticum*. Planted in parkland woods.

Common Wintergreen, *Pyrola minor* (PYROLA-CEAE). Last recorded 1878.

PLUMBAGINACEAE
Thrift, *Armeria maritima*. Platelayer's derelict garden (02J).
‡ *Limonium suworowii* (02J).

PRIMULACEAE (p. 72)
Blue Pimpernel, *Anagallis foemina*. Garden weed: 06M, 24Y, (95N, 06T).
Bog P., *A. tenella*. Marshes (95X). Site drained c. 1967.
'Hoaxlip', *Primula veris* × *P. vulgaris*. Woods: 95J, 96W, 05T, 13D, 15G.
Primula elatior × *P. vulgaris*. 25K(Q).
‡ **Dotted Loosestrife**, *Lysimachia punctata*. 92E (02J).

‡ **Butterfly-bush**, *Buddleja davidii*. (BUDDLEJACEAE). 92IV, 02AFV, 12F, 13TUW, 15M, 24N.

OLEACEAE (p. 73)
‡ **Lilac**, *Syringa vulgaris*. A planted tree. 93T, 03I, 04F, 11D.

APOCYNACEAE (p. 73)
‡ **Greater Periwinkle**, *Vinca major*. 92H, 03EF, 04HLN, 05CF, 11E, 13P, 14CK.

GENTIANACEAE (p. 73)
Early Gentian, *Gentianella anglica*. Chalk downland. Last recorded c. 1930.

MENYANTHACEAE (p. 74)
Fringed Water-lily, *Nymphoides peltata*. Pond: 04P. Status not known.
‡ **Jacob's-ladder**, *Polemonium caeruleum* (POLEMONIA-CEAE). (03M).

BORAGINACEAE (p. 74)
Amsinckia intermedia. Only record 1923.
A. menziesii. Only record 1924.
‡ **Alkanet**, *Anchusa azurea*. 05G, 15G (05F, 12F).
‡ **Borage**, *Borago officinalis*. 14E (02F).
Green Hound's-tongue, *Cynoglossum germanicum*. Wood border (94X).
§ *Echium plantagineum* (*E. lycopsis*).
§ *Heliotropium europaeum*.
§ *Lappula squarrosa* (*L. echinata, L. myosotis*).
Purple Gromwell, *Lithospermum purpurocaeruleum*. Only record 1875. Status not known.
Wood Forget-me-not, *Myosotis sylvatica*. Garden escape only: 05FG, 12F.
‡ **Blue-eyed-Mary**, *Omphalodes verna*. 04J.
‡ **Green Alkanet**, *Pentaglottis sempervirens*. 92DIL, 95N, 03G, 13N, 15R.
Lungwort, *Pulmonaria officinalis*. Last record c. 1930. Status not known.
Creeping Comfrey, *Symphytum grandiflorum*. Naturalised in old garden: 93Y.
Previous records of *S. asperum* are all probably in error.
Abraham-Isaac-Jacob, *Trachystemon orientalis*. Only record 1880.

HYDROPHYLLACEAE
Nemophila menziesii. Only record 1928. Status not known.
Phacelia tanacetifolia. Garden weed: 04P.

CONVOLVULACEAE (p. 76)
* *Cuscuta campestris*. 93W (03N).
Flax Dodder, *C. epilinum*. Last recorded c. 1920.
Dodder, *C. epithymum*. Parasite on various species (92D, 93HM, 95N, 03V, 05C, 14A). Last recorded c. 1950.
‡ **Hairy Bindweed**, *Calystegia pulchra*. Hedgerows near houses: 92Y, 02EFS, 04J, 15G.
* **Yam**, *Ipomoea batatas*. (12F).

SOLANACEAE (p. 76)
§ *Datura ferox*.
* *Hyoscyamus albus*. 05F.
‡ **China Teaplant**, *Lycium chinense*. Hedgerows usually near houses. Recorded for 46 tetrads.
§ *Nicandra physalodes*.
§ *Nicotiana occidentalis, N. suaveolens*.
‡ *N. rustica*. (92I).
‡ **Cape-gooseberry**, *Physalis alkekengi*. 92V, 93F, 02QV, 05A, 12F, 14H, 15U.
§ *Physalis acutifolia, P. ixocarpa*.
§ *Solanum cornutum* (*S. rostratum*), *S. sisymbrifolium, S. triflorum*.

SCROPHULARIACEAE (p. 77)
‡ **Snapdragon**, *Antirrhinum majus*. 11EI, 14G (03H).
‡ **Fairy Foxglove**, *Erinus alpinus*. 03X, 06H.
Mudwort, *Limosella aquatica*. Muddy shores of lakes (93L).

§ **Purple Toadflax**, *Linaria purpurea*. Recorded for 32 tetrads.
‡ *Linaria maroccana*. (14Z).
L. purpurea × *L. repens*. (02A).
L. repens × *L. vulgaris*. 02FJQV, 11E, 12A.
Common Cow-wheat, *Melampyrum pratense*. Woods. Last recorded c. 1930.
‡ **Monkeyflower**, *Mimulus guttatus*. (11I, 23I).
‡ **Musk**, *M. moschatus*. (93L).
Marsh Lousewort, *Pedicularis palustris*. Marshes. Last recorded c. 1926.
Lousewort, *P. sylvatica*. Damp pastures (92J, 93VW, 03M).
‡ **Moth Mullein**, *Verbascum blattaria*. 95N.
‡ **Orange M.**, *V. phlomoides*. 92H, 05G, 12F, 13J, 15Q.
‡ **Twiggy M.**, *V. virgatum*. 03H.
Hoary M., *V. pulverulentum*. Only record 1875.
Veronica anagallis-aquatica × *V. catenata*. 15T (13P).

LENTIBULARIACEAE (p. 81)
Butterwort, *Pinguicula vulgaris*. Last recorded 1921 (on chalk downland).
Lesser Bladderwort, *Utricularia minor*. Last recorded 1798.
Greater B., *U. vulgaris*. Last recorded 1889.

VERBENACEAE (p. 81)
§ *Verbena bonariensis*, *V. menthaefolia*, *V. supina*.

LABIATAE (p. 82)
§ *Dracocephalum parviflorum*.
Large-flowered Hemp-nettle, *Galeopsis speciosa*. Arable land (03M, 04N).
Galeopsis bifida. The complete distribution not yet known but it appears to be no less common than *G. tetrahit* sensu stricto with which it often grows.
‡ **Spotted Dead-nettle**, *Lamium maculatum*. 03Y, 05C, 12F (02L, 15R).
Motherwort, *Leonurus cardiaca*. Last recorded 1798.
‡ **Balm**, *Melissa officinalis*. 02U (92P).
* **White Horehound**, *Marrubium vulgare*. (92H, 02V, 12A). Also frequent as a wool alien.
‡ *Mentha* × *gentilis*. 02QW, 16Q (01I, 02A).
‡ **Horse Mint**, '*M. longifolia*'. Recorded for 18 tetrads.
‡ **Apple M.**, '*M.* × *niliaca*'. 92I, 02P, 04B, 05GM, 12B, 14R, 24C.
Pennyroyal, *M. pulegium*. Last recorded 1907.
‡ **Spear Mint**, *M. spicata*. 92I, 93N, 02FQ, 04P, 05K, 06AP, 12B, 25F.
M. aquatica × *M. arvensis* (*M.* × *verticillata*). 03L, (92DI, 93L, 02I, 06H).
‡ *Nepeta mussini*. (02J).
Cut-leaved Selfheal, *Prunella laciniata*. Garden lawn (15G).
Prunella laciniata × *P. vulgaris*. 15G.
‡ **Meadow Clary**, *Salvia pratensis*. 02A.
* *Salvia reflexa*. 02CJ, 03G, 05G, 12F. Occurs also as a wool alien.
S. nemorosa ('*S.* × *sylvestris*'). Only record 1889.
‡ **Whorled Clary**, *S. verticillata*. Waste places (02H, 03V, 96V).
Stachys annua. Arable fields (03V).
Downy Woundwort, *S. germanica*. Last recorded 1801.
S. palustris × *S. sylvatica*. (23D).
Wall Germander, *Teucrium chamaedrys*. Last recorded 1798.

PLANTAGINACEAE (p. 85)
Plantago indica. (02J).
P. ovata. (02J).

CAMPANULACEAE (p. 86)
‡ *Campanula bononiensis*. (04K).
‡ **Canterbury-bells**, *C. medium*. 02IMR, 03I, 11E.
C. patula. Last recorded 1889.
Legousia speculum-veneris. Arable fields (02Y).

RUBIACEAE (p. 87)
Slender Bedstraw, *Galium pumilum*. Pastures (02K). Status not known.
Corn Cleavers, *G. tricornutum* (*G. tricorne*). Still frequent in 1953 as a cornfield weed on calcareous soil. Now known as a weed in only one garden: 02F.
§ *Galium setaceum*.
G. mollugo × *G. verum*. (02A, 03A, 14P).

CAPRIFOLIACEAE (p. 88)
Perfoliate Honeysuckle, *Lonicera caprifolium*. Last recorded 1889. Status not known.
Fly H., *L. xylosteum*. Last recorded c. 1900. Status not known.
‡ **Snowberry**, *Symphoricarpos rivularis*. Hedgerows near to houses. Recorded for 78 tetrads.

VALERIANACEAE (p. 89)
Hairy-fruited Cornsalad, *Valerianella eriocarpa*. (92E). Status not known.

DIPSACACEAE (p. 90)
* **Fuller's Teasel**, *Dipsacus sativus*. (02W, 12F).

COMPOSITAE (p. 90)
§ *Acanthospermum australe*.
Achillea millefolium subsp. *tanacetifolia*. Only record 1884.
§ *A. nobilis*.
* *Ambrosia trifida*. (15R).
§ *Amellus microglossus*, *A. strigosus*.
Mountain Everlasting, *Antennaria dioica*. Chalk downland. Last recorded 1926.
‡ **Yellow Chamomile**, *Anthemis tinctoria*. 03K, 06N, 23IJ.
Arctium tomentosum. 02I, appearing regularly.
Lamb's Succory, *Arnoseris minima*. Sandy fields. Last recorded c. 1930.
§ *Artemisia afra*, *A. dracunculus*.
Chinese Mugwort, *A. verlotiorum*. Waste places: 92R.
Michaelmas Daisies, *Aster* spp. These are frequent as garden escapes but no attempt has been made to account for the species concerned.
§ *Berkheya heterophylla*.
§ *Bidens bipinnata*, *B. pilosa*, *B. vulgata*.
* **Beggar-ticks**, *B. frondosa*. 92D, 02V, (03M 11E).
‡ **Field Marigold**, *Calendula arvensis*. 92I, 03S (02J).
‡ **Pot M.**, *C. officinalis*. 92I, 93U, 02BC, 05FG, 12F, 24E.
§ *Calotis cuneifolia*, *C. dentex*, *C. hispidula*, *C. lappulacea*.
§ *Carduus argentatus*, *C. pycnocephalus*, *C. tenuifolius*.
§ *Carthamus lanatus*.
* **Safflower**, *C. tinctorius*. 05G (02J).
§ *Centaurea calcitrapa*, *C. melitensis*, *C. solstitialis*.
Cornflower, *C. cyanus*. Occurs now only as a garden escape.
* *C. diluta*. 92I, 05G, 12F, 14S, 24E.
§ *Chrysanthemum coronarium*. *C. myconis*.
§ *Chrysocoma tenuifolia*.
‡ **Blue Sow-thistle**, *Cicerbita macrophylla*. 92E, 13R, 24M.
Chicory, *Cichorium intybus*. A relic of cultivation. Recorded for 13 tetrads.
§ *Cichorium endivia*, *C. pumilum*.
§ *Cineraria lyratus*.
§ *Conyza bonariensis* (*Erigeron b.*), *C. sumatrensis* (*C. floribunda*).
‡ *Cosmos bipinnatus*. 05G (02J).
§ *Cotula australis*.

* **Bristly Hawk's-beard**, *Crepis setosa*. 02A, 03V.
  Crepis nicaeensis. Last recorded 1894.
  C. sancta. Only record 1922.
§ *Cryptostemma calendulacea*.
  Red-tipped Cudweed, *Filago lutescens* (*F. apiculata*).
  Last recorded 1908.
  Broad-leaved C., *F. pyramidata* (*F. spathulata*). Last
  recorded 1882.
* *Guizotia abyssinica*. 92I, 93U, 02BC, 04M, L5F, 12F.
* **Sunflower**, *Helianthus annuus*. 92I, 93U, 02BC, 04M,
  05F, 12F.
‡ *Helianthus rigidus*. 92I, 02BC, 05G, 12F.
§ *Helichrysum odoratissimum*.
  Hawkweeds (*Hieracium* spp.). In addition to those species
  for which maps are provided the following are re-
  corded. They occur mainly in rough grassland and on
  railway banks.
  Hieracium diaphanum (including *H. anglorum*). 03G, 04AF,
  05E, 06X, 24A (93P 96L, 03T).
  H. exotericum. 95P, 96L (96R).
  H. grandidens. 96V.
  H. lepidulum. 96R.
  H. maculatum. 03F.
  H. pellucidum. (96R).
  H. pulmonarioides. Only record 1885.
  H. rigens. (03Y).
  H. salticola. 04A.
  H. sublepistoides. 14C (96R, 05BE).
  H. vagum. 92B, 03I, 04U, 06A, 14F (96R, 02M, 03FG).
  H. vulgatum. 14F.
  Smooth Cat's-ear, *Hypochoeris glabra*. Sandy fields (14Z,
  24E). Occurs also as a wool alien.
§ *Ifloga verticillata*.
§ *Inula graveolens*.
  Lapsana intermedia. Railway bank, well established:
  92W.
§ *Lasiospermum pedunculare*.
‡ **Shasta Daisy**, *Leucanthemum maximum*. 92I, 05G (02J).
§ *Madia sativa*.
§ *Matricaria occidentalis*.
‡ **Cotton Thistle**, *Onopordon acanthium*. 13X. Occurs also
  as a wool alien.
§ *Pentzia grandiflora*.
‡ **White Butterbur**, *Petasites albus*. (03J).
‡ **Fox-and-cubs**, *Pilosella aurantiaca* subsp. *brunneocrocea*
  (*Hieracium brunneocroceum*). Dry banks: 01I, 04C, 06V,
  13P, 15M.
  Pilosella praealta subsp. *arvorum*. 05DE.
  Small Fleabane, *Pulicaria vulgaris*. Last recorded 1864.
§ *Schkuhria pinnata*.
* *Scolymus hispanicus*. 04Z (12A).
§ *Senecio arenarius*, *S. bipinnatisectis*, *S. inaequidens*, *S.
  pterophorus*.
  S. squalidus × *S. viscosus* (*S.* × *londinensis*). 92R, 93Z,
  02R, 03I, 13W, 14X, 15A.
  S. squalidus × *S. vulgaris*. 02V, 03I.
§ *Sigesbeckia microcephala*, *S. orientalis*.
§ **Milk Thistle**, *Silybum marianum*.
‡ **Canadian Goldenrod**, *Solidago canadensis*. 92I, 94U,
  02BC, 04Z, 05FG, 12F, 13P, 14I, 24E.
§ *Soliva anthemifolia*.
  Marsh Sow-thistle, *Sonchus palustris*. Roadsides, well
  established: 06J.
  Sonchus tenerrimus. Only record 1933.
§ *Tagetes minuta*.
  Dandelions (*Taraxacum* spp.). This genus has been the
  subject of recent revision and the distribution of the
  many segregates in the county demands attention.
‡ **Salsify**, *Tragopogon porrifolius*. (03T, 04P).
§ *Verbesina encelloides*.
§ *Vittadinia australis* (*V. triloba*).
§ *Xanthium ambrosoides*, *X. spinosum*, *X. strumarium*.

ALISMATACEAE (p. 100)
Lesser Water-plantain, *Baldellia ranunculoides*. Ditches:
15R (15T).

HYDROCHARITACEAE (p. 100)
Frogbit, *Hydrocharis morsus-ranae*. Pond: 04P. Status not
known.

POTAMOGETONACEAE (p. 101)
Red Pondweed, *Potamogeton alpinus*. Flooded pits (13U,
14E).
Bog P., *P. polygonifolius*. Last recorded 1886.
Hairlike P., *P. trichoides*. Only record 1930.
Potamogeton × *lintonii* (*P. crispus* × *P. friesii*). 15M.

LILIACEAE (p. 102)
Asparagus, *Asparagus officinalis*. Relic of cultivation.
Railway banks, usually well established. Recorded for
12 tetrads.
§ *Asphodelus fistulosus*.
Meadow Saffron, *Colchicum autumnale*. Naturalised in
old garden: 14Y.
‡ **Spanish Bluebell**, *Endymion hispanicus*. 24N.
Fritillary, *Fritillaria meleagris*. Wet meadows (92K).
Site ploughed c. 1967.
‡ **Martagon Lily**, *Lilium martagon*. Naturalised in woods:
95XY (long established), 96F, 06U.
May Lily, *Maianthemum bifolium*. Only record 1837.
‡ **Grape Hyacinth**, *Muscari atlanticum*. 06F (25F).
‡ *Muscari comosum*. (02Q).
Bog Asphodel, *Narthecium ossifragum*. Last recorded
1798.
Drooping Star-of-Bethlehem, *Ornithogalum nutans*.
Last recorded 1846.
‡ **Solomon's-seal**, *Polygonatum* × *hybridum*. 14M (long
established), 03A, (95TY 03U).
Butcher's-broom, *Ruscus aculeatus*. Planted in park-
land woods.
Wild Tulip, *Tulipa sylvestris*. Last recorded 1841.
* **Date**, *Phoenix dactylifera* (PALMACEAE). Seedlings only
(02J, 12F, 14N).

JUNCACEAE (p. 103)
Saltmarsh Rush, *Juncus gerardii*. Gravel pit (15U).
Slender R., *J. tenuis*. Gravel pit (15U).
§ *Juncus pallidus*. With other Australian species including
J. australis, *J. gregiflorus*, *J. procerus*, *J. sarophorus*, *J.
usitatus*, *J. vaginatus* and hybrids with British species.
Gravel pits (14E, 15TU).
J. acutiflorus × *J. articulatus*. 92Z, 02D.
J. effusus × *J. inflexus*. 92Z, 02D.

AMARYLLIDACEAE (p. 105)
‡ *Allium moly*. (02J).
‡ **Few-flowered Leek**, *A. paradoxum*. 93J.
‡ **Snowdrop**, *Galanthus nivalis*. 93P, 95V, 02BG, 14F, 15G.
‡ **Summer Snowflake**, *Leucojum aestivum*. Lakeside, long
established: 02B.
‡ **Primrose-peerless**, *Narcissus* × *medioluteus* (*N.* ×
biflorus). Naturalised: 01DE.

IRIDACEAE (p. 105)
‡ **Blue-eyed-grass**, *Sisyrinchium bermudiana*. (15U).

ORCHIDACEAE (p. 105)
Early Marsh-orchid, *Dactylorhiza incarnata* (*Dactylorchis
i.*). Marshes (92V, 16V).
Heath Spotted-orchid, *D. maculata* (*Dactylorchis m.*)
Heaths (03M). Site ploughed 1962.
Dactylorhiza maculata × *D. praetermissa*. (03M).
Marsh Helleborine, *Epipactis palustris*. Chalk downland:
91Z. Status not known.

Gymnadenia conopsea subsp. *densiflora*. Chalk downland (02P).

Bog Orchid, *Hammarbya paludosa*. Last recorded 1798.

Lizard Orchid, *Himantoglossum hircinum*. Chalk downland (02P).

Early Spider-orchid. *Ophrys sphegodes*. Only record c. 1800.

LEMNACEAE (p. 108)

Greater Duckweed, *Lemna polyrhiza*. Ditches and ponds (92I, 14X, 15U, 24P). Last recorded 1953.

CYPERACEAE (p. 109)

Green-ribbed Sedge, *Carex binervis*. Heaths (93G).

White S., *C. curta*. Heaths (92H, 03M).

Common Yellow-sedge, *C. demissa*. Marshes (92E).

Dioecious Sedge, *C. dioica*. Only record 1805.

Divided S., *C. divisa*. Only record 1920. Status not known.

Tufted-sedge, *C. elata*. Last recorded 1911.

Tawny Sedge, *C. hostiana*. Marshes (92W).

§ *Carex inversa*.

Long-stalked Yellow-sedge, *C. lepidocarpa*. Marshes (92W, 02C).

Flea Sedge, *C. pulicaris*. Last record 1898.

C. hostiana × *C. lepidocarpa*. (92W).

C. otrubae × *C. remota*. (*C. pseudoaxillaris*). (02J).

§ *Cyperus eragrostis*.

* *C. esculentus*. (12F).

C. longus. (04P), probably planted.

* *C. rotundus*. (02J).

Needle Spike-rush, *Eleocharis acicularis*. Last definite record 1802.

White Beak-sedge, *Rhynchospora alba*. Last recorded 1798.

Black Bog-rush, *Schoenus nigricans*. Last recorded 1798.

Deergrass, *Scirpus cespitosus*. Last recorded 1798.

Sea Club-rush, *S. maritimus*. Flooded pit (15U).

Grey C., *S. tabernaemontani*. Flooded pits and lakes (93L, 14E, 15U). Means of introduction not known.

GRAMINEAE (p. 113)

§ *Agropyron scabrum*.

§ *Agrostis avenacea*, *A. lachnantha*, *A. semiverticillata*.

Orange Foxtail, *Alopecurus aequalis*. Muddy shores of ponds (92DI, 03A).

§ *Amphibromus neesii*.

Annual Vernal-grass, *Anthoxanthum puelii*. Bare sandy ground. Last record 1919.

Apera interrupta. Bare ground: 13S, status not known.

* **Loose Silky-bent**, *A. spica-venti*. (03I).

§ *Aristida benthamii*, *A. congesta*.

§ *Arrhenatherum album*.

§ *Avena barbata*.

* **Bristle Oat**, *A. strigosa*. (02J).

§ *Briza maxima*, *B. minor*.

Field Brome, *Bromus arvensis*. Field borders: 24G.

Rye B., *B. secalinus* Arable fields: 04R, 24F.

Bromus squarrosus. Only record c. 1884.

§ *B. carinatus*, *B. diandrus*, *B. fasciculatus*, *B. ferronii* (*B. molliformis*), *B. lanceolatus* (*B. japonicus*), *B. madritensis*, *B. rigidus*, *B. rubens*, *B. scoparius*, *B. tectorum*, *B. unioloides*.

§ *Cenchrus ciliaris*, *C. echinatus*.

§ *Chloris divaricata*, *C. truncata*, *C. virgata*.

§ *Cynodon dactylon*, *C. incompletus*.

* **Rough Dog's-tail**, *Cynosurus echinatus*. 15N (03M 15U).

§ *Dactyloctenium radulans*.

§ *Danthonia caespitosa*, *D. penicillata*.

§ *Dichanthium sericeum*.

§ *Digitaria ciliaris* (*adscendens*), *D. ctenantha*.

* *D. sanguinalis*. 05F (01Z, 03M).

§ *Diplachne fusca*, *D. muelleri*.

* *Echinochloa colonum*. (02J).

§ *E. crus-galli*.

* *E. utilis* ('*E. frumentacea*'). 92I, 02BC, 05G, 12F, 24E.

§ *Ehrharta longiflora*.

§ *Eleusine africana*, *E. multiflora*, *E. tristachya*.

Elymus arenarius. (01DE). Status not known.

§ *Eragrostis cilianensis*, *E. curvula*, *E. dielsii*, *E. lehmanniana*, *E. molybdea*, *E. neomexicana*, *E. parviflora*, *E. poaeoides*, *E. trachycarpa*.

§ *Eriochloa creba*, *E. pseudo-acrotricha*.

Various-leaved Fescue, *Festuca heterophylla*. Coppice: 96G.

Hard F., *F. longifolia*. Railway banks (92W, 96LQ, 02J, 04A, 11I).

§ *Gastridium phleoides*, *G. ventricosum*.

§ *Glyceria multiflora*, *G. spicata*.

§ *Helictotrichon turgidulum*.

Foxtail Barley, *Hordeum jubatum*. Introduced with grass seed: 92J, 93N, 02Y, 05K, 16Q.

§ *Hordeum flexuosum*, *H. glaucum*, *H. hystrix*, *H. leporinum*, *H. marinum*, *H. procera*, *H. pubiflorum*, *H. pusillum*.

§ *Koeleria phleoides*.

§ *Lamarckia aurea*.

§ *Lolium loliaceum*, *L. rigidum*.

L. multiflorum × *L. perenne*. 03N.

* **Darnel**, *L. temulentum*. 02C, 05FG, 24E (02J, 03H, 13X).

Early Sand-grass, *Mibora minima*. Garden weed (01Z).

§ *Microleana stipoides*.

§ *Monerma cylindrica*.

Mat-grass, *Nardus stricta*. Heaths (92D). Last recorded c. 1955.

§ *Nasella trichotoma*.

§ *Oryzopsis miliacea*.

* **Millet**, *Panicum miliaceum*. 92I, 02BC, 04M, 05FG, 12F, 24E.

§ *Panicum capillare*, *P. decompositum*, *P. laevifolium*, *P. prolutum*, *P. subalbidum*.

§ *Parapholis incurva*.

§ *Paspalidium jubiflorum*.

§ *Paspalum dilatatum*.

§ *Phalaris brachystachys*, *P. minor*, *P. tuberosa*.

* *P. paradoxa*. 05G. Occurs also as a wool alien.

§ *Poa sterilis*.

§ *Polypogon maritimus*. (93L).

§ *P. monspeliensis*.

§ *Rhynchelytrum villosum*.

§ *Schmidtia kalaharensis*.

* *Setaria geniculata*. 12F. Occurs also as a wool alien.

* *S. glauca* (*S. lutescens*). 92I, 02C, 03M, 05G, 12F, 24E.

* *S. italica*. 92I, 03M, 05G, 12F.

* *S. verticillata*. 05F. Also occurs as a wool alien.

* *S. viridis*. 92I, 02BC, 04LM, 05FG, 12F, 24E.

* *Sorghum bicolor*. 12F.

§ *S. halepense*.

§ *Sporobolus africanus*.

§ *Stipa ambigua* (*S. dusenii*), *S. aristiglumis*, *S. capensis* (*S. tortilis*), *S. formicarum*, *S. hyalina*, *S. neesiana*, *S. verticillata*.

§ *Trachynia distachya*.

§ *Tragus australianus*, *T. berteronianus*, *T. koelerioides*, *T. racemosus*.

* *Vulpia megalura*. (03H, 11I).

§ *V. australis*, *V. geniculata*.